PANCREA

CANCER DIET

COOKBOOK

Beginner-Friendly Nutritious and Delicious Recipes to Fight Inflammation, Manage Pain, and Improve Quality of Life

MARY B. LAX

DISCLAIMER NOTICE

The recipes and information provided are for general informational purposes only. The author/publisher is not liable for any adverse effects resulting from the use of this cookbook. Readers are advised to use their best judgment and seek professional advice when necessary.

DEDICATION

This book is dedicated to everyone who's been affected by pancreatic cancer - patients, caregivers, family, and friends. Your strength and courage inspire us every day.

To the patients: You face each day bravely, even when it's tough. Your spirit is amazing.

To the caregivers: You're always there, helping and caring for your loved ones. Your love means everything.

To the families: You stick together through thick and thin, giving support and love.

To the friends: You're there with a kind word or a helping hand when it's needed most.

This book is for you all. Let's keep fighting together for a better future.

TABLE OF CONTENTS

SOUPS 62

DESSERTS 74

A LETTER TO YOU

Dear Reader,

I'm writing to you from the depths of my heart, with every word filled with empathy and understanding. If you're holding this cookbook in your hands, chances are you or someone you love is facing the daunting journey of pancreatic cancer. I want you to know that you're not alone.

Facing pancreatic cancer is undoubtedly challenging, but amidst the difficulties, something is empowering about taking control of what we can – our diet and nutrition. That's where this cookbook comes in. It's more than just a collection of recipes; it's a guide to nourishing your body and spirit during this difficult journey.

As you explore the recipes within these pages, I hope you'll find comfort in knowing that each one has been carefully crafted with simplicity and ease in mind. Whether you're a seasoned chef or new to the kitchen, these recipes are designed to be accessible to everyone. Because in times of struggle, good food should be simple and comforting.

Beyond the recipes, I hope you'll find solace in the fact that you're not alone. You're part of a community of fighters, survivors, caregivers, and champions. Together, we're stronger than any disease, and together, we'll navigate this journey with courage, grace, and love.

So, dear reader, as you embark on this culinary journey, may each meal bring you strength, nourishment, and a reminder of the resilience that lies within you.

Sincerely,
Mary B. Lax.

HOW TO USE THIS COOKBOOK

To make the most of this cookbook, here are some tips on how to use it effectively:

1. **Browse Through**: Start by browsing through the recipes to get a sense of what's included. Take note of any dishes that catch your eye or ingredients that you're curious about.

2. **Read Instructions Thoroughly**: Before you begin cooking, carefully read through the instructions for each recipe. Note any special techniques or equipment needed and make sure you understand all the steps.

3. **Gather Ingredients**: Once you've chosen a recipe to try, gather all the ingredients you'll need. Check your pantry and make a shopping list for any items you don't already have.

4. **Preparation**: Prep all your ingredients before you start cooking. This includes chopping vegetables, measuring out spices, and preheating your oven or stovetop.

5. **Follow Recipe Steps**: Follow the recipe steps closely, taking care to measure ingredients accurately and cook according to the specified times and temperatures.

6. **Weekly Meal Plan Session**: Take advantage of the weekly meal plan session, where you'll find curated recipes for each day of the week. You'll also find helpful prep tips for each recipe to help streamline your cooking process.

7. **Taste and Adjust**: Don't be afraid to taste your dish as you go and adjust seasoning or flavors to suit your preferences. Cooking is an art, and recipes are just guidelines – feel free to get creative!

8. **Presentation**: Once your dish is ready, take a moment to plate it up nicely. Presentation can make a big difference in how a dish is perceived and enjoyed.

9. **Enjoy**: Finally, sit down and enjoy your delicious creation! Whether you're cooking for yourself, family, or friends, take pleasure in the fruits of your labor and savor every bite.

10. **RECIPE JOURNAL BONUS**: As a special bonus, you'll receive a 10-page recipe journal to accompany your culinary journey. Use it to jot down your own recipes, make notes on recipe modifications, or simply record your cooking adventures.

Remember, cooking is meant to be fun and rewarding, so don't stress too much about getting everything perfect. Experiment, learn from your mistakes, and most importantly, have fun in the kitchen!

OVERVIEW OF THE PANCREATIC CANCER

EXPLANATION OF PANCREATIC CANCER AND ITS IMPACT ON DIET

Pancreatic cancer is a serious disease that develops in the tissues of the pancreas, an organ located behind the stomach. This type of cancer often goes undetected in its early stages due to the lack of specific symptoms, leading to diagnosis at more advanced stages when treatment options may be limited.

The impact of pancreatic cancer on diet can be significant, as the pancreas plays a crucial role in digestion by producing enzymes that help break down food and hormones that regulate blood sugar levels. When the pancreas is affected by cancer, it can lead to various complications that affect a person's ability to eat and absorb nutrients effectively.

Some common challenges related to diet and pancreatic cancer include:

1. **Appetite Loss**: Cancer and its treatments such as chemotherapy and radiation therapy can cause loss of appetite, making it difficult for patients to consume an adequate amount of food.
2. **Digestive Issues**: Pancreatic cancer can impair the production of digestive enzymes, leading to problems with digestion and absorption of nutrients. This can result in symptoms like diarrhea, bloating, and weight loss.
3. **Nutritional Deficiencies**: Poor appetite and digestive issues can contribute to nutritional deficiencies, including deficiencies in essential vitamins and minerals like vitamin D, calcium, and iron.
4. **Malnutrition**: Prolonged inadequate intake of nutrients can lead to malnutrition, which weakens the body's ability to fight off infections, tolerate cancer treatments, and recover from surgery.
5. **Changes in Taste and Smell**: Cancer treatments can alter a person's sense of taste and smell, making certain foods less appealing or even unpleasant to eat.
6. **Difficulty Swallowing**: Pancreatic tumors can press on the nearby organs, causing difficulty swallowing (dysphagia) or a feeling of fullness even after consuming small amounts of food.

IMPORTANCE OF DIET IN PANCREATIC CANCER MANAGEMENT

Diet plays a pivotal role in the comprehensive management of pancreatic cancer, offering a multifaceted approach to support both the physical and emotional well-being of individuals facing this challenging diagnosis. The significance of a well-considered diet in pancreatic cancer management extends beyond mere sustenance; it becomes a cornerstone in enhancing the quality of life, mitigating treatment-related side effects, and potentially influencing the course of the disease.

1. **Nourishing the Body**: A wholesome and balanced diet is crucial for providing the body with the essential nutrients needed for overall health. In the context of pancreatic cancer, where nutritional challenges are prevalent, maintaining an adequate intake of proteins, healthy fats, vitamins, and minerals becomes instrumental. These nutrients not only support the immune system but also contribute to the body's ability to withstand the rigors of cancer treatments.

2. **Mitigating Weight Loss**: Pancreatic cancer often leads to unintended weight loss, which can exacerbate the already compromised health of individuals. A carefully curated diet aims to address this issue by focusing on nutrient-dense foods and tailored caloric intake. Strategies such as incorporating calorie-dense foods and utilizing healthy fats can help counteract weight loss, contributing to improved energy levels and enhanced overall well-being.

3. **Alleviating Treatment Side Effects**: The treatments for pancreatic cancer, including chemotherapy and radiation therapy, can introduce a myriad of side effects that impact nutritional intake. Nausea, vomiting, and changes in taste perception can deter individuals from consuming adequate and nourishing meals. Dietary modifications, such as opting for smaller, more frequent meals and exploring various cooking techniques to enhance flavor, play a pivotal role in managing these treatment-related challenges.

4. **Maintaining Nutrient Absorption**: The pancreatic enzymes responsible for breaking down and absorbing nutrients may be compromised due to the cancer itself or the treatments undergone. A diet tailored to accommodate these limitations often involves adjustments such as opting for easily digestible foods, considering enzyme supplements, and exploring alternative cooking methods to enhance nutrient absorption.

5. **Emotional Well-Being**: Beyond the physiological aspects, diet also influences the emotional and psychological well-being of individuals grappling with pancreatic cancer. The act of sharing nourishing meals with loved ones, savoring familiar flavors, and finding joy in the sensory experience of eating can contribute to a sense of normalcy and comfort during a challenging time.

6. **Empowering Personalized Care**: Recognizing the individuality of each patient is paramount in pancreatic cancer management. Tailoring dietary recommendations to align with personal preferences, cultural backgrounds, and specific health needs fosters a sense of empowerment. Collaborating closely with healthcare professionals, including dietitians, ensures that the dietary approach is personalized, flexible, and responsive to the evolving needs of the individual.

DIETARY CONSIDERATIONS DURING TREATMENT

During treatment for pancreatic cancer, dietary considerations play a crucial role in managing symptoms, supporting overall health, and optimizing treatment outcomes. Here are some important dietary guidelines to consider during this challenging time:

1. **Maintain Adequate Nutrition**: Pancreatic cancer and its treatments can lead to side effects such as nausea, vomiting, and appetite changes, which may compromise nutritional intake. It's essential to prioritize consuming enough calories and nutrients to support the body's energy needs and immune function. Eating small, frequent meals and snacks rich in protein, healthy fats, and carbohydrates can help meet nutritional requirements.

2. **Stay Hydrated**: Dehydration is a common concern during cancer treatment, particularly if experiencing symptoms like vomiting or diarrhea. Aim to drink plenty of fluids throughout the day, including water, herbal teas, and clear broths. Electrolyte-rich beverages like coconut water can also help replenish lost fluids and minerals.

3. **Manage Digestive Symptoms**: Many individuals undergoing treatment for pancreatic cancer experience digestive issues such as diarrhea, constipation, or bloating. Adjusting your diet to include easily digestible foods, such as steamed vegetables, lean proteins, and whole grains, can help alleviate discomfort. Avoiding spicy, greasy, or overly processed foods may also help manage digestive symptoms.

4. **Focus on Nutrient-Dense Foods**: Opt for nutrient-dense foods that provide essential vitamins, minerals, and antioxidants to support overall health and immune function. Include a variety of colorful fruits and vegetables, whole grains, lean proteins, and healthy fats in your diet. Nutrient-rich foods can help optimize healing, reduce inflammation, and support the body's natural defense mechanisms.

5. **Consider Supplemental** Nutrition: In some cases, individuals may struggle to meet their nutritional needs through diet alone due to treatment side effects or difficulty eating. In such instances, healthcare providers may recommend oral nutritional supplements or enteral feeding to ensure adequate nutrient intake. These supplements can provide additional calories, protein, vitamins, and minerals to support recovery and maintain nutritional status.

6. **Manage Weight Changes**: Weight loss or unintended weight gain can occur during pancreatic cancer treatment, impacting overall health and treatment tolerance. Work closely with a registered dietitian or healthcare provider to monitor weight changes and adjust your diet as needed. They can provide personalized nutrition counseling and support to help you achieve and maintain a healthy weight throughout treatment.

7. **Listen to Your Body**: Pay attention to your body's cues and adjust your diet based on how you're feeling. If certain foods trigger symptoms or exacerbate side effects, consider temporarily eliminating or reducing them from your diet. Experiment with different foods and cooking methods to find what works best for you.

FOODS TO EAT AND AVOID

When it comes to pancreatic cancer, making dietary choices that support overall health and well-being is crucial. Here's a guide to foods to eat and avoid for pancreatic cancer:

Foods to Eat:

- **Fruits and Vegetables**: Choose a variety of colorful fruits and vegetables, such as berries, citrus fruits, leafy greens, broccoli, and bell peppers. These foods are rich in vitamins, minerals, and antioxidants, which can help support immune function and reduce inflammation.

- **Whole Grains**: Incorporate whole grains like brown rice, quinoa, oats, and whole wheat bread into your diet. These grains provide fiber, which can aid in digestion and help regulate blood sugar levels.

- **Lean Proteins**: Opt for lean sources of protein such as poultry, fish, tofu, legumes, and nuts. Protein is essential for tissue repair and immune function, especially during cancer treatment.

- **Healthy Fats**: Include sources of healthy fats in your diet, such as avocados, olive oil, nuts, and seeds. These fats provide energy and support the absorption of fat-soluble vitamins.

- **Herbal Teas**: Enjoy herbal teas such as ginger tea, chamomile tea, or green tea. These beverages can help soothe digestive discomfort and provide hydration without added sugar or caffeine.

Foods to Avoid or Limit:

- **Processed Meats**: Avoid processed meats such as bacon, sausage, hot dogs, and deli meats, as they are high in saturated fats and sodium, which may increase inflammation and cardiovascular risk.

- **Sugary Foods and Beverages**: Limit your intake of sugary foods and beverages like candy, soda, pastries, and sweetened cereals. Excess sugar intake can contribute to weight gain and inflammation.

- **Fried and High-Fat Foods**: Limit fried foods, fast food, and foods high in unhealthy fats such as butter, margarine, and hydrogenated oils. These foods can be difficult to digest and may exacerbate digestive symptoms.

- **Alcohol**: Limit alcohol consumption, as it can contribute to dehydration, liver damage, and increased cancer risk. If you choose to drink alcohol, do so in moderation and consider opting for red wine in small amounts.

- **Refined Carbohydrates**: Reduce your intake of refined carbohydrates like white bread, white rice, and sugary cereals. These foods can cause blood sugar spikes and provide little nutritional value.

- **Excessive Caffeine**: Limit your intake of caffeinated beverages such as coffee, tea, and energy drinks, as they can contribute to dehydration and may worsen digestive symptoms in some individuals.

BREAKFAST RECIPES

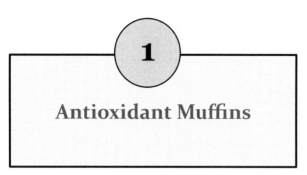

Antioxidant Muffins

Prep Time: 10 minutes

Cook Time: 30-40 minutes

Servings: 6-8 muffins

Ingredients:

- 1 cup whole wheat flour
- 1/3 cup brown sugar
- 1/2 teaspoon baking powder
- 1/3 cup pecans, chopped
- 1/4 teaspoon salt
- 1 cup blueberries
- 1/4 cup almond milk
- 1 large egg

Instructions:

1. Preheat the oven to 350°F (175°C, gas mark 4). Line a muffin tin with paper liners or lightly grease the muffin cups.

2. In a large mixing bowl, combine the whole wheat flour, brown sugar, baking powder, chopped pecans, and salt. Stir until well mixed.

3. In a separate bowl, lightly beat the egg, then add the almond milk. Stir to combine the wet ingredients.

4. Pour the wet ingredients into the dry ingredients and stir until just combined. Be careful not to overmix; a few lumps in the batter are okay.

5. Gently fold in the blueberries until evenly distributed throughout the batter.

6. Spoon the batter into the prepared muffin cups, filling each about two-thirds full.

7. Bake in the preheated oven for 30 to 40 minutes, or until a toothpick inserted into the center of a muffin comes out clean.

8. Once baked, remove the muffins from the oven and allow them to cool in the muffin tin for 5 minutes. Then, transfer the muffins to a wire rack to cool completely.

9. Serve the muffins warm or at room temperature. Enjoy!

Variation and Tips:

- ✓ Substitute other berries such as raspberries or blackberries for the blueberries for a variation in flavor.

- ✓ For added texture and flavor, sprinkle a little extra chopped pecans on top of each muffin before baking.

- ✓ These muffins can be stored in an airtight container at room temperature for up to 3 days or frozen for longer storage. Simply thaw frozen muffins at room temperature or reheat them in the microwave before serving.

Nutrition Information
(Approximate, per serving):
Calories: 180 Carbohydrates: 31g Fiber:
3g Sugars: 14g Fat: 5g Protein: 4g
Sodium: 110mg

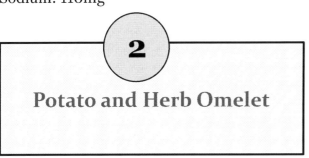

2
Potato and Herb Omelet

Prep Time: 15 minutes
Cook Time: 25 minutes
Servings: 4 (1 omelet per serving)
Ingredients:

- 1 lb. potatoes, peeled and diced or shredded
- 2 tablespoons extra-virgin olive oil
- 1/2 cup diced red onion
- 2 cloves garlic, minced
- 4 large whole eggs, lightly beaten
- 2 egg whites, lightly beaten
- 2 tablespoons finely chopped fresh parsley
- 2 tablespoons finely chopped fresh basil and chives
- Salt, to taste
- Sprigs of fresh herbs to garnish (optional)

Instructions:

1. Place the diced or shredded potatoes in a large pan. Cover with water and bring to a boil. Cook uncovered for 3 minutes. Remove from heat, cover, and let stand for 10 minutes until potatoes are tender but not mushy. Drain well.

2. Heat olive oil in a deep 10-inch non-stick skillet over medium heat. Add diced red onion and minced garlic. Cook for 8 minutes, stirring occasionally, until onions are translucent and garlic is fragrant.

3. Add the cooked potatoes to the skillet. Cook for an additional 5 minutes, stirring occasionally, until potatoes are golden brown and crispy on the edges.

4. In a mixing bowl, combine lightly beaten whole eggs and egg whites. Stir in chopped parsley, basil, and chives. Season with salt to taste.

5. Evenly pour the egg mixture over the potatoes in the skillet. Reduce heat to low and cook uncovered for about 10 minutes, or until the bottom of the omelet is golden and the top is set.

6. Optionally, place the skillet under a toaster oven to lightly brown the top of the omelet.

7. Garnish with sprigs of fresh herbs if desired. Serve immediately

Variation and Tips:

✓ Customize the herbs to your preference or based on what you have available.

✓ Feel free to add other vegetables such as bell peppers or spinach for added flavor and nutrition.

✓ Serve with a side salad or whole grain toast for a complete meal.

Nutrition Information (Approximate, per serving):

Calories: 240 Carbohydrates: 23g Fiber: 2g Sugar: 2g Fat: 12g Protein: 11g Sodium: 105mg

3

Ricotta and Strawberry Basil Toast

Prep Time: 5 minutes

Cook Time: 5 minutes

Servings: 1

Ingredients:

- 1 slice whole grain bread, toasted
- 1 tablespoon ricotta cheese
- 3 fresh basil leaves, sliced into strips
- 2-4 strawberries, sliced into thin strips

Instructions:

1. Toast the whole grain bread until golden brown and crispy.

2. Spread the ricotta cheese evenly over the toasted bread.

3. Arrange the sliced strawberries on top of the ricotta cheese.

4. Sprinkle the sliced basil leaves over the strawberries.

5. Serve immediately and enjoy the delicious combination of savory ricotta cheese, sweet strawberries, and fragrant basil on whole grain toast.

Variation and Tips:

✓ Experiment with different types of berries such as raspberries, blueberries, or blackberries for variety.

✓ Drizzle a little honey or balsamic glaze over the toast for added sweetness and flavor.

✓ Garnish with a sprinkle of chopped nuts or a drizzle of olive oil for extra texture and richness.

✓ Serve as a light breakfast, snack, or appetizer any time of day.

Nutrition Information (Approximate, per serving):

Calories: 140 Carbohydrates: 23g Fiber: 3g Fat: 4g Protein: 5g Sodium: 135mg

Pumpkin Spice Overnight Oats

Prep Time: 5 minutes

Chill Time: Overnight

Servings: 1

Ingredients:

- 1/2 cup rolled oats
- 1/2 cup unsweetened almond milk (or any type of milk)
- 1/3 cup plain, reduced-fat Greek yogurt
- 1 tablespoon ground flaxseed
- 2 tablespoons pumpkin puree
- 1 tablespoon maple syrup
- 1/2 teaspoon vanilla extract
- 1/2 teaspoon ground cinnamon
- 1/4 teaspoon ground ginger
- 1/4 teaspoon ground nutmeg
- Pinch of salt

Instructions:

1. In a Mason jar or airtight container, combine rolled oats, unsweetened almond milk, Greek yogurt, ground flaxseed, pumpkin puree, maple syrup, vanilla extract, ground cinnamon, ground ginger, ground nutmeg, and a pinch of salt.

2. Stir the ingredients together until well combined.

3. Seal the container and refrigerate overnight, or for at least 4 hours, to allow the oats to soften and the flavors to meld.

4. In the morning, give the oats a good stir. If desired, add a splash of additional almond milk for a creamier consistency.

5. Serve the pumpkin spice overnight oats cold, straight from the refrigerator. Enjoy!

Variation and Tips:

✓ For added crunch and texture, top the oats with chopped nuts, such as pecans or walnuts, or a sprinkle of granola before serving.

✓ Customize the sweetness to your preference by adjusting the amount of maple syrup or adding a drizzle of honey.

✓ Feel free to add extras like raisins, dried cranberries, or chopped apples for more flavor and nutrition.

✓ Make a batch of overnight oats at the beginning of the week for a quick and convenient breakfast option throughout the week.

Nutrition Information (Approximate, per serving):
Calories: 340 Carbohydrates: 52g Fiber: 8g Sugar: 17g Fat: 7g Protein: 16g Sodium: 270mg

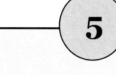

5

Apricot Pecan Breakfast Bars

Prep Time: 15 minutes

Cook Time: 25 minutes

Servings: 24

Ingredients:

- 3 cups quick-cooking oats
- 1/2 cup chopped pecans
- 3 cups unsweetened grain cereal (such as Cheerios or shredded wheat)
- 2 cups dried apricots, chopped
- 1/4 cup whole-wheat flour
- 12 oz. silken tofu, drained
- 1 large egg
- 1/2 cup applesauce
- 1/2 cup canola oil
- 3/4 cup honey
- 1/2 teaspoon salt
- 1 tablespoon freshly grated lemon zest
- 1 tablespoon vanilla extract
- Canola oil cooking spray

Instructions:

1. Preheat the oven to 350°F (175°C). Lightly coat a 9x13-inch baking dish with canola oil cooking spray.

2. In a large mixing bowl, combine the quick-cooking oats, chopped pecans, unsweetened grain cereal, chopped dried apricots, and whole-wheat flour. Mix well.

3. In a blender or food processor, blend the silken tofu until smooth.

4. In a separate mixing bowl, whisk together the blended silken tofu, egg, applesauce, canola oil, honey, salt, lemon zest, and vanilla extract until well combined.

5. Pour the wet mixture over the dry ingredients in the large mixing bowl. Stir until all ingredients are evenly combined and coated.

6. Transfer the mixture to the prepared baking dish, spreading it out evenly and pressing it down firmly with the back of a spoon or spatula.

7. Bake in the preheated oven for 25-30 minutes, or until the edges are golden brown and the bars are set in the center.

8. Remove from the oven and let cool completely in the baking dish on a wire rack.

9. Once cooled, cut into 24 bars. Store the apricot pecan breakfast bars in an airtight container at room temperature for up to one week, or freeze for longer storage.

Variation and Tips:

✓ Substitute other dried fruits such as raisins, cranberries, or chopped dates for the apricots for variety.

✓ For added sweetness, drizzle melted dark chocolate over the cooled bars before serving.

✓ Experiment with different nuts such as almonds, walnuts, or cashews for a different flavor profile.

✓ Enjoy these breakfast bars on-the-go or as a convenient snack any time of day.

Nutrition Information (Approximate, per serving):

Calories: 190 Carbohydrates: 30g Fiber: 3g Sugar: 15g Fat: 8g Protein: 4g Sodium: 55mg

6

Peanut Butter Banana Chia Toast

Prep Time: 5 minutes

Cook Time: 5 minutes

Servings: 1

Ingredients:

- 1 slice whole grain bread, toasted
- 1 tablespoon peanut butter
- 1/2 banana, sliced
- 1 teaspoon chia seeds (or flaxseed)

Instructions:

1. Toast the whole grain bread until golden brown and crispy.

2. Spread the peanut butter evenly over the toasted bread.

3. Arrange the sliced banana on top of the peanut butter.

4. Sprinkle chia seeds (or flaxseed) over the banana slices for added texture and nutrients.

5. Serve immediately and enjoy the classic combination of peanut butter, banana, and chia seeds on whole grain toast.

Variation and Tips:

✓ Substitute almond butter for peanut butter for a different flavor profile.

✓ Experiment with other toppings such as sliced strawberries, blueberries, or a drizzle of honey for added sweetness.

✓ Chia seeds can be omitted if desired, but they provide additional fiber, protein, and omega-3 fatty acids.

✓ This toast makes for a quick and nutritious breakfast or snack option, providing a good balance of healthy fats, carbohydrates, and protein.

Nutrition Information (Approximate, per serving):

Calories: 250 Carbohydrates: 34g Fiber: 8g Sugar 12g Fat: 10g Protein: 10g Sodium: 220mg

7

Cottage Cheese, Cucumber, and Tomato Toast

Prep Time: 5 minutes

Cook Time: 5 minutes

Servings: 1

Ingredients:

- 1 slice whole grain bread, toasted
- 1/4 cup low-fat cottage cheese
- 4-5 thin cucumber slices
- 2-3 thin tomato slices, cut into quarters
- Cracked black pepper (to taste)

Instructions:

1. Toast the whole grain bread until golden brown and crispy.
2. Spread the low-fat cottage cheese evenly over the toasted bread.
3. Arrange the thin cucumber slices on top of the cottage cheese.
4. Place the thin tomato slices on top of the cucumber slices.
5. Sprinkle cracked black pepper over the tomato slices to taste.

6. Serve immediately and enjoy the delightful combination of creamy cottage cheese, crisp cucumber, and juicy tomato on whole grain toast.

Variation and Tips:

- ✓ Add a sprinkle of fresh herbs such as basil or dill for extra flavor.
- ✓ Substitute cottage cheese with Greek yogurt for a different taste and texture.
- ✓ Experiment with other vegetables such as sliced bell peppers or radishes for variety.
- ✓ This toast makes for a light and refreshing breakfast or snack option, perfect for any time of the day.

Nutrition Information (Approximate, per serving):

Calories: 150 Carbohydrates: 20g Fiber: 3g Sugar 8g Fat: 3g Protein: 12g Sodium: 320mg

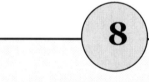

8

Quinoa Breakfast Bowl

Prep Time: 5 minutes

Cook Time: 15 minutes

Servings: 2

Ingredients:

- 1/2 cup quinoa, rinsed

- 1 cup water or low-sodium vegetable broth
- 1/4 teaspoon ground cinnamon
- 1/2 cup unsweetened almond milk
- 1 tablespoon honey or maple syrup
- 1/4 cup chopped nuts (almonds, walnuts, or pecans)
- 1/4 cup fresh berries (blueberries, strawberries, or raspberries)
- 1 tablespoon ground flaxseed
- Optional toppings: sliced banana, chopped apple, dried fruits, coconut flakes

Instructions:

1. In a small saucepan, combine quinoa, water or vegetable broth, and ground cinnamon. Bring to a boil, then reduce heat to low, cover, and simmer for 12-15 minutes, or until quinoa is cooked and water is absorbed.
2. Once cooked, fluff the quinoa with a fork and divide it into two serving bowls.
3. In a separate small saucepan, warm the almond milk over low heat. Stir in honey or maple syrup until dissolved.
4. Pour the warm almond milk mixture over the cooked quinoa in each bowl.
5. Top each bowl with chopped nuts, fresh berries, and ground flaxseed.
6. Add any optional toppings you prefer, such as sliced banana, chopped apple, dried fruits, or coconut flakes.
7. Serve immediately and enjoy your nutrient-packed quinoa breakfast bowl!

Variation and Tips:

✓ For added protein, stir in a spoonful of Greek yogurt or a sprinkle of chia seeds.
✓ Customize your bowl with your favorite fruits and nuts based on personal preferences and seasonal availability.
✓ Substitute almond milk with any other plant-based milk like soy milk or oat milk if preferred.

Nutrition Information (Approximate, per serving):

Calories: 300 Carbohydrates: 45g Fiber: 6g Sugar: 12g Fat: 10g Protein: 8g Sodium: 50mg

9

Purple Grape Jam Pancakes

Prep Time: 10 minutes

Cook Time: 20 minutes

Servings: 4

Ingredients for the Jam:

- 2 cups purple grapes, cut in half

- 2 tablespoons lemon juice
- 1 teaspoon honey
- 1/4 teaspoon ground cinnamon
- Pinch of salt, or to taste
- 1 teaspoon cornstarch
- 1 tablespoon water

Ingredients for the Pancakes:

- 1 cup chickpea flour
- 2 teaspoons baking powder
- 1/4 teaspoon ground cinnamon
- Pinch of salt, or to taste
- 3/4 cup plain unsweetened almond milk
- 1 teaspoon honey
- 1/2 teaspoon vanilla extract
- Nonstick cooking spray
- 4 tablespoons almond or peanut butter

Instructions for the Jam:

1. In a small saucepan, combine the purple grapes, lemon juice, honey, ground cinnamon, and salt.
2. Cook over medium heat, stirring occasionally, until the grapes start to break down and release their juices, about 5-7 minutes.
3. In a small bowl, mix together the cornstarch and water to create a slurry.
4. Stir the slurry into the grape mixture and continue to cook, stirring constantly, until the mixture thickens, about 2-3 minutes.

5. Remove from heat and set aside.

Instructions for the Pancakes:

1. In a large mixing bowl, whisk together the chickpea flour, baking powder, ground cinnamon, and salt.
2. In a separate bowl, mix together the almond milk, honey, and vanilla extract.
3. Pour the wet ingredients into the dry ingredients and stir until just combined. Be careful not to overmix; a few lumps are okay.
4. Heat a nonstick skillet or griddle over medium heat and lightly coat with nonstick cooking spray.
5. Pour 1/4 cup of the pancake batter onto the skillet for each pancake. Cook until bubbles form on the surface, then flip and cook until golden brown on the other side, about 2-3 minutes per side.
6. Repeat with the remaining batter, spraying the skillet with more cooking spray as needed.
7. Serve the pancakes warm, topped with a spoonful of the homemade grape jam and a dollop of almond or peanut butter.
8. Enjoy your delicious and nutritious purple grape jam pancakes!

Variation and Tips:

✓ Feel free to use any other fruit jam or spread of your choice if you prefer.

✓ You can substitute chickpea flour with whole wheat flour or all-purpose flour if desired.

✓ Serve with additional fresh fruit, nuts, or a drizzle of maple syrup for extra flavor and sweetness.

✓ These pancakes are perfect for a cozy breakfast or brunch treat that's both satisfying and wholesome.

Nutrition Information (Approximate, per serving):

Calories: 240 Carbohydrates: 29g Fiber: 5g Sugar: 14g Fat: 11g Protein: 9g Sodium: 45mg

10

Breakfast Quesadillas

Prep Time: 10 minutes

Cook Time: 10 minutes

Servings: Makes 2 quesadillas

Ingredients:

- 2 whole wheat tortillas
- 4 eggs
- 1/4 cup black beans
- 1/4 cup diced tomatoes
- 1/4 cup shredded cheddar cheese
- Salt and pepper to taste
- 1 tablespoon olive oil

Instructions:

1. In a mixing bowl, beat the eggs and season with salt and pepper according to taste.

2. Heat olive oil in a skillet over medium heat. Pour in the beaten eggs and scramble until cooked through.

3. Lay one tortilla flat on a clean surface. Spread half of the scrambled eggs evenly over one half of the tortilla.

4. Sprinkle half of the black beans, diced tomatoes, and shredded cheddar cheese over the eggs.

5. Fold the empty half of the tortilla over the filling, creating a half-moon shape.

6. Repeat the process with the remaining tortilla and filling ingredients.

7. Heat a non-stick skillet over medium heat. Place one quesadilla in the skillet and cook for 2-3 minutes on each side, or until golden brown and crispy.

8. Remove from the skillet and let it cool slightly before slicing into wedges.

9. Serve warm and enjoy your delicious breakfast quesadillas!

Variations and Tips:

✓ Customize your quesadillas by adding your favorite ingredients such as avocado slices, cooked bacon or sausage, bell peppers, or spinach.

- ✓ For a spicy kick, add some diced jalapeños or a dash of hot sauce to the filling.
- ✓ Make it a wholesome meal by serving with a side of salsa, sour cream, or guacamole.
- ✓ These quesadillas can be enjoyed for breakfast, brunch, or even as a quick and satisfying dinner option.

Nutrition Information (Approximate):

Calories: 360 kcal Carbohydrates: 27 g Fiber: 5 g Sugars: 2 g Fat: 20 g Protein: 20 g Sodium: 560 mg

SALADS

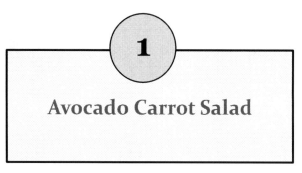

Avocado Carrot Salad

Prep Time: 10 minutes

Servings: 2

Ingredients:

- 1 large avocado, peeled, pitted, and diced
- 4 medium carrots, peeled and grated
- Dash of balsamic vinegar
- Sunflower seeds, to taste
- Salt and freshly ground pepper, to taste

Instructions:

1. In a mixing bowl, combine the diced avocado and grated carrots.
2. Drizzle a dash of balsamic vinegar over the avocado and carrot mixture.
3. Add sunflower seeds to the bowl according to your preference.
4. Season the salad with salt and freshly ground pepper to taste.
5. Gently toss all the ingredients together until well combined.
6. Serve the avocado carrot salad immediately as a refreshing side dish or light lunch option.
7. Enjoy the vibrant flavors and textures of this simple yet delicious salad!

Variation and Tips:

✓ For added freshness and flavor, consider adding chopped herbs such as parsley, cilantro, or dill.

✓ You can also add a squeeze of fresh lemon or lime juice for a citrusy twist.

✓ Customize the salad by incorporating additional vegetables such as cucumber, bell peppers, or cherry tomatoes.

✓ Feel free to adjust the seasoning and vinegar to suit your taste preferences.

Nutrition Information (Approximate):

Calories: 200 Protein: 4g Carbohydrates: 15 g Fiber: 8 g Sugars: 4 g Fat: 15 g Sodium: 150mg

Broccoli Apple Salad

Prep Time: 15 minutes

Chill Time: 30 minutes

Servings: 6

Ingredients:

- 4 cups fresh broccoli florets
- 1/2 cup dried cranberries
- 1/2 cup sunflower seeds
- 3 organic apples, diced
- 1/4 cup red onion, chopped

- 1 cup plain, low-fat yogurt with probiotic bacteria
- 2 tablespoons Dijon-style mustard
- 1/4 cup honey

Instructions:

1. In a large mixing bowl, combine the fresh broccoli florets, dried cranberries, sunflower seeds, diced apples, and chopped red onion.
2. In a separate small bowl, whisk together the plain yogurt, Dijon-style mustard, and honey until well combined.
3. Pour the yogurt dressing over the broccoli mixture in the large bowl.
4. Gently toss all the ingredients together until the salad is evenly coated with the dressing.
5. Cover the bowl and refrigerate for at least 30 minutes to allow the flavors to meld together.
6. Once chilled, give the salad a final toss and adjust seasoning if necessary.
7. Serve the broccoli apple salad chilled as a refreshing side dish or light meal option.
8. Enjoy the crisp and flavorful combination of broccoli, apples, and tangy yogurt dressing!

Variations and Tips:

✓ Add a handful of chopped pecans or almonds for extra crunch and nuttiness.
✓ For a savory twist, toss in some crumbled feta cheese or goat cheese.
✓ Substitute the dried cranberries with raisins or chopped dates for a different flavor profile.
✓ If you prefer a creamier dressing, mix in some mayonnaise or Greek yogurt along with the Dijon-style mustard and honey.
✓ Enhance the salad's freshness with a squeeze of lemon juice or a sprinkle of fresh herbs like parsley or dill.
✓ Customize the salad by incorporating other fruits like grapes or pears for added sweetness and texture.
✓ To make it a complete meal, add grilled chicken strips or chickpeas for protein.
✓ For a vegan version, swap the honey for maple syrup or agave nectar and use dairy-free yogurt.

Nutrition Information (Approximate):

Calories: 220 Protein: 8g Carbohydrates: 30 g Fiber: 7 g Sugars: 15 g Fat: 9g Fat: 1g Sodium: 150 mg

3

Strawberry Fennel Salad

Prep Time: 15 minutes

Servings: 4

Ingredients:

- 2 tablespoons extra-virgin olive oil
- 1 tablespoon white wine vinegar
- 200 g (7 oz) lettuce, shredded
- 1 large head fennel, thinly sliced
- 1/2 organic cucumber, thinly sliced
- 10 large strawberries, quartered
- 1/2 cup roughly chopped walnuts

Instructions:

1. In a small bowl, whisk together the extra-virgin olive oil and white wine vinegar to create the dressing.

2. In a large salad bowl, combine the shredded lettuce, thinly sliced fennel, cucumber, quartered strawberries, and chopped walnuts.

3. Drizzle the dressing over the salad ingredients.

4. Gently toss the salad to ensure even coating of the dressing.

5. Serve the Strawberry Fennel Salad immediately as a refreshing side dish or light meal.

6. Enjoy the vibrant combination of flavors and textures!

Variation and Tips:

✓ Add a sprinkle of crumbled feta cheese or goat cheese for a creamy and tangy flavor.

✓ For an extra burst of freshness, toss in some freshly chopped mint or basil leaves.

✓ Substitute the walnuts with sliced almonds or pecans for a different nutty flavor.

✓ If strawberries are not in season, you can use other berries like raspberries or blueberries for a similar fruity taste.

✓ To make it a heartier meal, add grilled chicken slices or cooked quinoa to the salad.

✓ Feel free to customize the dressing by adding a touch of honey or Dijon mustard for sweetness or tanginess, respectively.

✓ For a vegan option, swap the honey for maple syrup or agave nectar in the dressing.

Nutrition Information (Approximate):

Calories: 180 Protein: 5g Carbohydrates: 10g Fiber: 4g Sugar: 5g Fat: 12g Sodium: 30mg

4

Arugula and Tomato Salad with Avocado

Prep Time: 10 minutes

Servings: 4

Ingredients:

- 3 cups young arugula leaves, rinsed
- 2 cups cherry tomatoes, halved
- 1/4 cup sun-dried tomatoes, chopped
- 2 tablespoons extra virgin olive oil
- 1 tablespoon balsamic vinegar
- 2 small avocados, peeled, pitted, and sliced

Instructions:

1. In a large salad bowl, combine the arugula leaves, halved cherry tomatoes, and chopped sun-dried tomatoes.
2. In a small bowl, whisk together the extra virgin olive oil and balsamic vinegar to create the dressing.
3. Drizzle the dressing over the salad ingredients.
4. Gently toss the salad to ensure even coating of the dressing.
5. Carefully add the sliced avocados to the salad.

6. Serve the Arugula and Tomato Salad with Avocado immediately as a refreshing side dish or light meal.
7. Enjoy the vibrant combination of peppery arugula, juicy tomatoes, creamy avocados, and flavorful dressing!

Variation and Tips:

- ✓ Add some crumbled feta cheese or goat cheese for an extra burst of flavor.
- ✓ Sprinkle toasted pine nuts or almonds over the salad for added crunch and texture.
- ✓ For a citrusy twist, squeeze some fresh lemon or lime juice over the salad before serving.

Nutrition Information (Approximate):

Calories: 300 Protein: 6g Carbohydrates: 15g Fiber: 10g Sugar: 8g Fat: 25g Sodium: 60mg

5

Pear and Radicchio Salad

Prep Time: 15 minutes

Servings: 4

Ingredients:

- 1 ½ cups shredded radicchio
- 3 cups shredded Romaine
- 2 small unpeeled pears (300 g), diced

- 2 oz unpeeled cucumber, diced
- 1.4 oz garden cress, trimmed
- 2 tsp extra virgin olive oil
- 2 tsp vinegar

Instructions:

1. In a large salad bowl, combine the shredded radicchio, shredded Romaine, diced pears, diced cucumber, and trimmed garden cress.
2. Drizzle extra virgin olive oil and vinegar over the salad ingredients.
3. Toss the salad gently until all ingredients are well coated with the dressing.
4. Serve the Pear and Radicchio Salad immediately as a refreshing side dish or light meal.

Variation and Tips:

✓ For added crunch, you can include toasted nuts such as walnuts or pecans.
✓ Add crumbled feta or goat cheese for a savory twist.
✓ Experiment with different types of vinegar, such as balsamic or apple cider vinegar, to enhance the flavor.

Nutrition Information (Approximate):

Calories: 90 Protein: 2g Carbohydrates: 15g Fiber: 3g Sugar: 10g Fat: 3g Sodium: 30mg

6

Smoked Salmon Salad

Prep Time: 15 minutes

Servings: 4

Ingredients:

- 1 small head of organic romaine lettuce
- 5 ounces smoked salmon, thinly sliced
- 2 tomatoes, diced
- 4 radishes, thinly sliced
- 1 organic carrot, diagonally sliced
- 1/2 cucumber, peeled and diced
- Juice of half a lemon
- 1 tsp fresh ginger root, peeled and minced
- 1 tbsp canola oil

Instructions:

1. Wash and chop the romaine lettuce into bite-sized pieces. Place them in a large salad bowl.
2. Add the thinly sliced smoked salmon, diced tomatoes, thinly sliced radishes, diagonally sliced carrot, and diced cucumber to the bowl.
3. In a small mixing bowl, whisk together the lemon juice, minced fresh ginger root, and canola oil to make the dressing.

4. Pour the dressing over the salad ingredients in the bowl.

5. Toss the salad gently to ensure even coating of the dressing.

6. Serve the Smoked Salmon Salad immediately as a refreshing and flavorful meal.

Variation and Tips:

✓ Feel free to add additional vegetables or greens such as bell peppers, spinach, or arugula for extra freshness and nutrition.

✓ For added texture and flavor, sprinkle some toasted nuts or seeds over the salad before serving.

✓ Customize the dressing by adding herbs like dill or parsley for a burst of freshness.

Nutrition Information (Approximate):

Calories: 150 Protein: 10g Carbohydrates: 5g Fiber: 4g Sugar: 2g Fat: 10g Sodium: 200mg

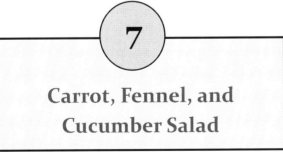

Carrot, Fennel, and Cucumber Salad

Prep Time: 15 minutes

Servings: 4

Ingredients:

- 6 organic carrots, thinly sliced
- 1 fennel bulb, thinly sliced
- 1 cucumber, thinly sliced
- 1 cup fresh parsley, chopped
- 4 tablespoons freshly squeezed lemon juice
- 2 tablespoons extra virgin olive oil
- Sea salt
- Freshly ground black pepper

Instructions:

1. In a large mixing bowl, combine the thinly sliced carrots, fennel bulb, cucumber, and chopped fresh parsley.

2. Drizzle the freshly squeezed lemon juice and extra virgin olive oil over the salad ingredients.

3. Season with sea salt and freshly ground black pepper according to taste.

4. Toss the salad gently to ensure even coating of the dressing and seasoning.

5. Serve the Carrot, Fennel, and Cucumber Salad immediately as a refreshing and nutritious side dish or light meal.

Variation and Tips:

✓ Add a sprinkle of toasted nuts or seeds for extra crunch and texture.

✓ For a hint of sweetness, consider adding a drizzle of honey or maple syrup to the dressing.

✓ Garnish the salad with some additional fresh herbs like mint or basil for added flavor.

Nutrition Information (Approximate, per serving):

Calories: 80 Protein: 2g Carbohydrates: 15g Fiber: 6g Sugar: 4g Fat: 4g Sodium: 100mg

8

Cucumber and Tomato Salad

Prep Time: 10 minutes

Servings: 4

Ingredients:

- 2 large cucumbers, peeled and coarsely chopped
- 3 large tomatoes, coarsely chopped
- 2/3 cup red onion, coarsely chopped
- 1/3 cup balsamic vinegar
- 1/2 tablespoon white sugar
- 3 tablespoons extra virgin olive oil
- Salt and pepper, to taste
- Fresh basil or mint leaves, for garnish (optional)

Instructions:

1. In a large mixing bowl, combine the chopped cucumbers, tomatoes, and red onion.

2. In a small bowl, whisk together the balsamic vinegar, white sugar, and extra virgin olive oil to make the dressing.

3. Pour the dressing over the cucumber and tomato mixture in the large bowl.

4. Season with salt and pepper according to taste.

5. Toss the salad gently to ensure even coating of the dressing and seasoning.

6. Garnish with fresh basil or mint leaves, if desired, before serving.

Variation and Tips:

✓ For added flavor, consider adding some crumbled feta cheese or sliced black olives.

✓ You can also customize the salad by adding other vegetables such as bell peppers or avocado.

✓ Adjust the amount of vinegar, sugar, and olive oil based on your personal preference for sweetness and acidity.

Nutrition Information (Approximate, per serving):

Calories: 120 Protein: 2g Carbohydrates: 10g Fiber: 3g Sugar: 6g Fat: 8g Sodium: 200mg

9

Beet and Carrot Salad

Prep Time: 10 minutes

Servings: 2

Ingredients:

- 1/2 cup raw beets, peeled and grated
- 1/2 cup organic carrots, grated
- 2 tablespoons apple juice
- 1 tablespoon extra-virgin olive oil
- 1/2 teaspoon fresh ginger, minced
- 1/8 teaspoon sea salt

Instructions:

1. In a mixing bowl, combine the grated beets and carrots.

2. In a small bowl, whisk together the apple juice, extra-virgin olive oil, minced ginger, and sea salt to make the dressing.

3. Pour the dressing over the grated beets and carrots.

4. Toss the salad gently until the vegetables are evenly coated with the dressing.

5. Let the salad sit for a few minutes to allow the flavors to meld together before serving.

Variation and Tips:

✓ Add a squeeze of fresh lemon juice for extra acidity and brightness.

✓ Garnish with chopped fresh herbs like parsley or cilantro for added flavor and freshness.

✓ For a touch of sweetness, sprinkle some raisins or dried cranberries over the salad.

✓ Adjust the seasoning according to your taste preferences.

Nutrition Information (Approximate, per serving):

Calories: 90 Protein: 2g Carbohydrates: 10g Fiber: 3g Sugar: 5-6 g Fat: 7g Sodium: 200mg Protein: 20 g

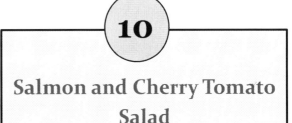

10

Salmon and Cherry Tomato Salad

Prep Time: 15 minutes

Servings: 2

Ingredients:

- 2 large fillets (9 oz) wild salmon, either poached or grilled and chilled in the fridge until cool
- 1 cup cherry tomatoes, halved
- 2 red onions, sliced
- 1 tablespoon capers
- 1 tablespoon fresh dill, finely chopped

- 1 tablespoon balsamic vinegar
- 1 tablespoon olive oil
- 1/4 teaspoon freshly ground black pepper
- Pinch of salt

Instructions:

1. In a large mixing bowl, flake the chilled salmon into bite-sized pieces using a fork.
2. Add the cherry tomatoes, sliced red onions, capers, and chopped fresh dill to the bowl with the salmon.
3. In a small bowl, whisk together the balsamic vinegar, olive oil, freshly ground black pepper, and a pinch of salt to make the dressing.
4. Pour the dressing over the salmon and vegetable mixture in the large bowl.
5. Gently toss all the ingredients together until well combined and evenly coated with the dressing.
6. Serve the salmon and cherry tomato salad immediately as a refreshing and nutritious meal option.

Variation and Tips:

✓ For added freshness and flavor, consider adding chopped fresh parsley or basil to the salad.
✓ Customize the salad by incorporating additional vegetables such as cucumber, bell peppers, or avocado.
✓ Adjust the seasoning and acidity of the dressing according to your taste preferences by adding more vinegar or olive oil as needed.
✓ Serve the salad over a bed of mixed greens or cooked quinoa for a heartier meal.

Nutrition Information (Approximate, per serving):

Calories: 300 Protein: 35g Carbohydrates: 15g Fiber: 3g Sugar: 5g Fat: 20g Sodium: 300mg

MAIN DISH

Herb-Marinated Chicken Breasts

Prep Time: 10 minutes

Cook Time: 20 minutes

Marinating Time: 30 minutes

Servings: 4

Ingredients:

- 4 boneless, skinless chicken breasts
- 2 tablespoons olive oil
- 2 tablespoons fresh lemon juice
- 1 tablespoon chopped fresh herbs (such as thyme, rosemary, or oregano)
- Salt and pepper to taste

Instructions:

1. In a small bowl, whisk together the olive oil, fresh lemon juice, chopped fresh herbs, salt, and pepper.
2. Place the chicken breasts in a shallow dish or a resealable plastic bag.
3. Pour the marinade over the chicken breasts, ensuring they are evenly coated. Massage the marinade into the chicken to ensure it's well distributed.
4. Cover the dish or seal the bag and refrigerate for at least 30 minutes to allow the flavors to meld and the chicken to marinate.
5. Preheat the grill or grill pan over medium-high heat. Brush the grates with oil to prevent sticking.
6. Remove the chicken breasts from the marinade and discard any excess marinade.
7. Place the chicken breasts on the grill and cook for 6-7 minutes per side, or until they are cooked through and no longer pink in the center. The internal temperature should reach 165°F (74°C).
8. Once cooked, transfer the chicken breasts to a serving platter and let them rest for a few minutes before serving.
9. Serve the herb-marinated chicken breasts hot with your favorite side dishes and enjoy!

Variation and Tips:

✓ Feel free to adjust the herbs according to your preference or what you have on hand.

✓ If you don't have fresh herbs, you can use dried herbs instead, but use half the amount since dried herbs are more concentrated in flavor.

✓ This marinade also works well with other proteins such as pork chops or fish fillets.

✓ Serve the chicken breasts alongside grilled vegetables, a fresh salad, or your favorite starch for a complete meal.

Nutrition Information (Approximate, per serving):

Calories 200 Fat: 15g Sodium: 300mg Carbohydrates: 0-1g Fiber: 0g Sugar: 0g Protein: 30g

2

Lemon Dill Salmon

Prep Time: 10 minutes

Cook Time: 12 minutes

Servings: 4

Ingredients:

- 4 salmon fillets
- 2 tablespoons olive oil
- 2 tablespoons fresh lemon juice
- 1 tablespoon chopped fresh dill
- Salt and pepper to taste

Instructions:

1. Preheat the oven to 400°F (200°C). Line a baking sheet with parchment paper or foil for easy cleanup.

2. Place the salmon fillets on the prepared baking sheet, skin-side down.

3. In a small bowl, whisk together the olive oil, fresh lemon juice, chopped fresh dill, salt, and pepper.

4. Drizzle the lemon dill mixture evenly over the salmon fillets, ensuring they are well coated.

5. Place the baking sheet in the preheated oven and bake for 10-12 minutes, or until the salmon is cooked through and flakes easily with a fork. The internal temperature should reach 145°F (63°C).

6. Once cooked, remove the salmon fillets from the oven and let them rest for a few minutes before serving.

7. Serve the lemon dill salmon hot with your favorite side dishes, such as roasted vegetables, rice, or a fresh salad.

Variation and Tips:

✓ Feel free to adjust the amount of fresh dill according to your preference.

✓ If you prefer a stronger lemon flavor, you can add more lemon juice to the marinade.

✓ For added flavor, you can sprinkle some lemon zest over the salmon before baking.

✓ This recipe can also be cooked on a grill. Simply preheat the grill to medium-high heat and grill the salmon for 4-5 minutes per side, or until cooked through.

✓ Leftover salmon can be stored in an airtight container in the refrigerator for up to 2 days. It's delicious served cold on top of salads or reheated gently in the microwave or oven.

Nutrition Information (Approximate, per serving):

Calories: 200 Fat: 4-6g Sodium: 400mgCarbohydrates: 30-35g Fiber: 10g Sugar: 8g Protein: 12g

3

Lentil Stir-Fry

Prep Time: 10 minutes

Cook Time: 25 minutes

Servings: 4

Ingredients:

- 1 cup brown lentils, rinsed and drained
- 2 cups water
- 1 tablespoon olive oil
- 1 onion, chopped
- 2 cloves garlic, minced
- 1 red bell pepper, chopped
- 1 zucchini, chopped
- 1 cup sliced mushrooms

- 2 tablespoons low-sodium soy sauce
- 1 tablespoon cornstarch
- Salt and pepper to taste

Instructions:

1. In a medium saucepan, combine the brown lentils and water. Bring to a boil, then reduce heat to low, cover, and simmer for 20-25 minutes, or until the lentils are tender and the water is absorbed. Remove from heat and set aside.

2. In a large skillet or wok, heat the olive oil over medium heat. Add the chopped onion and minced garlic, and sauté for 2-3 minutes, or until fragrant and translucent.

3. Add the chopped red bell pepper, zucchini, and sliced mushrooms to the skillet. Cook for 5-7 minutes, or until the vegetables are tender but still crisp.

4. In a small bowl, whisk together the low-sodium soy sauce and cornstarch until smooth.

5. Add the cooked lentils to the skillet with the vegetables. Pour the soy sauce mixture over the lentil and vegetable mixture, and toss to coat evenly.

6. Cook for an additional 2-3 minutes, or until the sauce has thickened slightly.

7. Season with salt and pepper to taste, and adjust seasoning as needed.

8. Serve the lentil stir-fry hot as a main dish or as a side dish alongside rice or quinoa.

Variation and Tips:

✓ Feel free to add other vegetables such as carrots, broccoli, or snow peas to the stir-fry for extra flavor and nutrition.

✓ You can substitute other types of lentils such as green or red lentils if preferred, adjusting the cooking time as needed.

✓ For added protein, you can stir in cooked tofu, chicken, or shrimp along with the lentils.

✓ Garnish with chopped green onions or cilantro for a pop of freshness and color before serving. Enjoy your hearty and nutritious lentil stir-fry!

Nutrition Information (Approximate, per serving):

Calories: 200-250 Fat: 6g Sodium: 400mg Carbohydrates: 35g Fiber: 8-10g Sugar: 8g Protein: 12g

4

Quinoa and Black Bean Salad

Prep Time: 15 minutes

Cook Time: 15 minutes

Servings: 4

Ingredients:

- 1 cup quinoa, rinsed and drained
- 2 cups water
- 1 can black beans, drained and rinsed
- 1 red bell pepper, chopped
- 1 avocado, diced
- 1/4 cup chopped cilantro
- 2 tablespoons lime juice
- 1 tablespoon olive oil
- Salt and pepper to taste

Instructions:

1. In a medium saucepan, combine the quinoa and water. Bring to a boil, then reduce heat to low, cover, and simmer for 15 minutes, or until the quinoa is cooked and water is absorbed. Remove from heat and let it cool.

2. In a large mixing bowl, combine the cooked quinoa, drained black beans, chopped red bell pepper, diced avocado, and chopped cilantro.

3. In a small bowl, whisk together the lime juice and olive oil. Pour the dressing over the quinoa mixture and toss until all ingredients are well coated.

4. Season the salad with salt and pepper to taste. Adjust seasoning as needed.

5. Serve the quinoa and black bean salad chilled or at room temperature.

Variation and Tips:

✓ Add diced tomatoes or corn kernels for additional color and flavor.

✓ For added protein, mix in grilled chicken, shrimp, or tofu.

✓ Garnish with extra cilantro or a sprinkle of feta cheese before serving.

✓ This versatile salad can be enjoyed as a main dish, a side dish, or even as a filling for wraps or burritos.

✓ Make it ahead of time and refrigerate for a refreshing and nutritious lunch or dinner option. Enjoy your delicious and wholesome quinoa and black bean salad!

Nutrition Information (Approximate, per serving):

Calories: 340 Fat: 15g Sodium: 200mg Carbohydrates: 45g Fiber: 13g Sugars: 2g Protein: 11g

5

Tofu Stir-Fry

Prep Time: 15 minutes

Cook Time: 15 minutes

Servings: 4

Ingredients:

- 1 block firm tofu, drained and sliced
- 2 tablespoons olive oil
- 2 tablespoons low-sodium soy sauce
- 1 tablespoon honey
- 1 tablespoon rice vinegar
- 1 teaspoon grated ginger
- 1 red bell pepper, sliced
- 1 zucchini, sliced
- 1 cup sliced mushrooms
- Salt and pepper to taste

Instructions:

1. Heat 1 tablespoon of olive oil in a large skillet or wok over medium-high heat.

2. Add the sliced tofu and cook for 5-7 minutes on each side, or until golden brown and crispy.

3. Remove the tofu from the skillet and set aside.

4. In the same skillet, add the remaining tablespoon of olive oil. Add the sliced

red bell pepper, zucchini, and sliced mushrooms. Cook for 5-7 minutes, or until the vegetables are tender-crisp.

5. In a small bowl, whisk together the low-sodium soy sauce, honey, rice vinegar, and grated ginger.

6. Return the cooked tofu to the skillet with the vegetables. Pour the soy sauce mixture over the tofu and vegetables. Stir well to coat everything evenly. Cook for an additional 2-3 minutes, or until the sauce has thickened slightly.

7. Season with salt and pepper to taste.

8. Serve the tofu stir-fry hot as a main dish or over cooked rice or noodles.

Variation and Tips:

✓ Feel free to add other vegetables such as broccoli, carrots, or snow peas to the stir-fry for extra flavor and nutrition.

✓ You can adjust the amount of honey or soy sauce according to your taste preferences.

✓ Garnish with sliced green onions or sesame seeds before serving for an extra burst of flavor.

✓ Leftover stir-fry can be stored in an airtight container in the refrigerator for up to 3 days. Reheat gently in the microwave or on the stovetop before

serving. Enjoy your delicious and nutritious tofu stir-fry!

Nutrition Information (Approximate, per serving):

Calories: 250 Fat: 15g Sodium: 450mg
Carbohydrates: 20g Fiber: 3g Sugars: 12g Protein: 12g

6

Garlic Shrimp Zoodles

Prep Time: 10 minutes
Cook Time: 10 minutes
Servings: 4

Ingredients:

* 1 lb raw shrimp, peeled and deveined
* 2 tablespoons olive oil
* 2 cloves garlic, minced
* 1/2 cup white wine
* 1/2 cup low-sodium chicken broth
* 1/4 cup chopped fresh parsley
* 1/4 cup chopped fresh basil
* 1/4 cup grated Parmesan cheese
* 4 medium zucchinis, spiralized
* Salt and pepper to taste

Instructions:

1. In a large skillet, heat the olive oil over medium heat. Add the minced

garlic and cook for 1-2 minutes, or until fragrant.

2. Add the raw shrimp to the skillet and cook for 2-3 minutes on each side, or until pink and cooked through. Remove the shrimp from the skillet and set aside.

3. Deglaze the skillet with white wine, scraping up any browned bits from the bottom of the pan. Allow the wine to simmer for 1-2 minutes to reduce slightly.

4. Add the low-sodium chicken broth to the skillet and bring to a simmer. Stir in the chopped fresh parsley and basil.

5. Return the cooked shrimp to the skillet and toss to coat in the sauce. Cook for an additional 1-2 minutes to heat through.

6. Meanwhile, spiralize the zucchinis into noodles using a spiralizer.

7. Add the spiralized zucchini noodles to the skillet with the shrimp and sauce. Toss everything together until the zucchini noodles are heated through and coated in the sauce.

8. Remove the skillet from heat and sprinkle grated Parmesan cheese over the top of the garlic shrimp zoodles.

9. Season with salt and pepper to taste, and serve hot.

Variation and Tips:

✓ You can add cherry tomatoes or sun-dried tomatoes to the skillet for extra flavor and color.

✓ For a creamy sauce, stir in a tablespoon of cream or coconut milk at the end.

✓ Garnish with additional chopped herbs and grated Parmesan cheese before serving.

✓ Leftover garlic shrimp zoodles can be stored in an airtight container in the refrigerator for up to 2 days. Reheat gently in the microwave or on the stovetop before serving. Enjoy your delicious and healthy garlic shrimp zoodles!

Nutrition Information (Approximate, per serving):

Calories: 280 Fat: 12g Sodium: 600mg
Carbohydrates: 10g Fiber: 2g Sugars: 3g
Protein: 30g

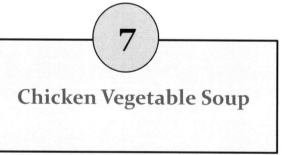

7

Chicken Vegetable Soup

Prep Time: 10 minutes
Cook Time: 25 minutes
Servings: 6

Ingredients:

- 1 lb boneless, skinless chicken thighs
- 2 cups low-sodium chicken broth
- 1 can diced tomatoes
- 1 cup sliced carrots
- 1 cup sliced celery
- 1 cup sliced cremini mushrooms
- 1/2 cup green peas
- 1/2 cup chopped onion
- 2 cloves garlic, minced
- 1 bay leaf
- 1 teaspoon dried thyme
- Salt and pepper to taste

Instructions:

1. In a large pot or Dutch oven, combine the chicken thighs, low-sodium chicken broth, diced tomatoes (including the juice), sliced carrots, sliced celery, sliced cremini mushrooms, green peas, chopped onion, minced garlic, bay leaf, and dried thyme.

2. Bring the soup to a boil over medium-high heat. Once boiling, reduce the heat to low and let the soup simmer for 20-25 minutes, or until the chicken is cooked through and the vegetables are tender.

3. Once the chicken is cooked, remove it from the pot and shred it using two forks. Return the shredded chicken to the pot and stir to combine.

4. Season the soup with salt and pepper to taste. Adjust seasoning as needed.

5. Remove the bay leaf before serving.

6. Ladle the chicken vegetable soup into bowls and serve hot.

Variation and Tips:

✓ Feel free to add other vegetables such as bell peppers, corn, or spinach to the soup for extra flavor and nutrition.

✓ You can use boneless, skinless chicken breasts instead of chicken thighs if preferred.

✓ For a thicker soup, you can add a tablespoon of flour mixed with water to the soup and let it simmer for an additional 5-10 minutes.

✓ Garnish with chopped fresh parsley or a squeeze of lemon juice before serving for a burst of freshness.

✓ Leftover soup can be stored in an airtight container in the refrigerator for up to 3 days. Reheat gently on the stovetop or in the microwave before serving. Enjoy your comforting and nutritious chicken vegetable soup!

Nutrition Information (Approximate, per serving):

Calories: 220 Fat: 6g Sodium: 300mg
Carbohydrates: 15g Fiber: 4g Sugars: 6g
Protein: 25g

8

Lentil Shepherd's Pie

Prep Time: 15 minutes

Cook Time: 45 minutes

Servings: 6

Ingredients:

For the Filling:

- 1 cup brown lentils, rinsed and drained
- 2 cups water
- 1 onion, chopped
- 2 cloves garlic, minced
- 1 cup sliced mushrooms
- 1 cup frozen peas and carrots
- 1 tablespoon tomato paste
- 1 tablespoon Worcestershire sauce
- 1 teaspoon dried thyme
- Salt and pepper to taste

For the Topping:

- 2 cups mashed sweet potato
- 1 tablespoon olive oil
- 1/4 cup chopped fresh parsley

Instructions:

1. Preheat your oven to 375°F (190°C).

2. In a large pot, combine the brown lentils and water. Bring to a boil, then reduce the heat to low and simmer for 20-25 minutes, or until the lentils are tender but not mushy. Drain any excess water and set aside.

3. In a separate skillet, heat olive oil over medium heat. Add the chopped onion and minced garlic, and cook for 2-3 minutes until softened.

4. Add the sliced mushrooms to the skillet and cook for an additional 5 minutes, or until they begin to brown.

5. Stir in the cooked lentils, frozen peas and carrots, tomato paste, Worcestershire sauce, dried thyme, salt, and pepper. Cook for another 5 minutes, stirring occasionally, until the mixture is heated through and well combined. Adjust seasoning to taste.

6. Transfer the lentil mixture to a baking dish and spread it out evenly.

7. In a bowl, mix together the mashed sweet potato with olive oil and chopped fresh parsley until well combined.

8. Spread the mashed sweet potato mixture over the lentil filling in the baking dish, covering it completely.

9. Place the baking dish in the preheated oven and bake for 20-25 minutes, or until the sweet potato topping is lightly golden brown and the filling is bubbling around the edges.

10. Remove from the oven and let it cool for a few minutes before serving.

11. Serve the lentil shepherd's pie hot, garnished with additional chopped parsley if desired.

Variation and Tips:

✓ Feel free to add other vegetables such as bell peppers, corn, or spinach to the lentil filling for extra flavor and nutrition.

✓ You can use regular mashed potatoes instead of sweet potato if preferred.

✓ Leftover shepherd's pie can be stored in an airtight container in the refrigerator for up to 3 days. Reheat gently in the microwave or oven before serving. Enjoy your hearty and nutritious lentil shepherd's pie!

Nutrition Information (Approximate, per serving):

Calories: 250 Fat: 6g Sodium: 400mg Carbohydrates: 45g Fiber: 10g Sugars: 10g Protein: 12g

9

Butternut Squash and Chickpea Curry

Prep Time: 15 minutes

Cook Time: 25 minutes

Servings: 4

Ingredients:

- 1 lb cubed butternut squash
- 1 can (15 oz) chickpeas, drained and rinsed
- 1 onion, chopped
- 2 cloves garlic, minced
- 1 tablespoon curry powder
- 1 teaspoon ground cumin
- 1 teaspoon ground coriander
- 1/2 teaspoon ground turmeric
- 1/2 teaspoon ground ginger
- 2 cups low-sodium vegetable broth
- 1/2 cup chopped fresh cilantro
- Salt and pepper to taste

Instructions:

1. In a large skillet or pot, heat a tablespoon of oil over medium heat. Add the chopped onion and minced garlic, and sauté for 2-3 minutes until softened.

2. Add the cubed butternut squash to the skillet and cook for another 5

minutes, stirring occasionally, until slightly tender.

3. Stir in the curry powder, ground cumin, ground coriander, ground turmeric, and ground ginger, and cook for 1-2 minutes until fragrant.

4. Add the drained and rinsed chickpeas to the skillet, along with the low-sodium vegetable broth. Stir to combine.

5. Bring the mixture to a simmer, then reduce the heat to low and let it simmer for 15-20 minutes, or until the butternut squash is tender and cooked through.

6. Once the butternut squash is cooked, season the curry with salt and pepper to taste. Adjust seasoning as needed.

7. Remove the skillet from heat and stir in the chopped fresh cilantro.

8. Serve the butternut squash and chickpea curry hot, garnished with additional cilantro if desired.

9. Enjoy your delicious and nutritious butternut squash and chickpea curry with rice, naan bread, or your favorite grain!

Variation and Tips:

✓ Feel free to add other vegetables such as spinach, kale, or bell peppers for extra flavor and nutrition.

✓ For added creaminess, stir in a splash of coconut milk or cashew cream at the end of cooking.

✓ Leftover curry can be stored in an airtight container in the refrigerator for up to 3 days. Reheat gently on the stovetop or in the microwave before serving.

Nutrition Information (Approximate, per serving):

Calories: 250 Fat: 3g Sodium: 300mg Carbohydrates: 50g Fiber: 12g Sugars: 8g Protein: 10g

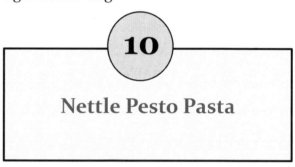

10

Nettle Pesto Pasta

Prep Time: 15 minutes

Cook Time: 10 minutes

Servings: 4

Ingredients:

- 2 cups young nettle leaves, blanched
- 4 garlic cloves, peeled
- 1/3 cup walnuts, chopped
- 1/3 cup Parmesan cheese, grated
- 1/3 cup extra-virgin olive oil
- 12 oz dried whole wheat pasta

Instructions:

1. Begin by blanching the nettle leaves. Bring a pot of water to a boil, then add

the nettle leaves and blanch them for 1-2 minutes. Remove the nettle leaves from the boiling water and immediately transfer them to a bowl of ice water to stop the cooking process. Drain the nettle leaves and set aside.

2. In a food processor, combine the blanched nettle leaves, peeled garlic cloves, chopped walnuts, and grated Parmesan cheese.

3. Pulse the ingredients together until they are finely chopped and well combined.

4. With the food processor running, gradually drizzle in the extra-virgin olive oil until the mixture forms a smooth paste. Stop and scrape down the sides of the food processor as needed.

5. Cook the dried whole wheat pasta according to the package instructions until al dente. Drain the cooked pasta, reserving a small amount of the cooking water.

6. In a large mixing bowl, toss the cooked pasta with the nettle pesto until the pasta is evenly coated. If the pesto is too thick, you can thin it out with a bit of the reserved pasta cooking water.

7. Serve the nettle pesto pasta hot, garnished with additional grated Parmesan cheese and chopped walnuts if desired.

8. Enjoy your flavorful and nutritious nettle pesto pasta!

Variation and Tips:

✓ Feel free to adjust the quantities of garlic, walnuts, and Parmesan cheese to suit your taste preferences.

✓ You can substitute other types of nuts such as pine nuts or almonds for the walnuts.

✓ For a vegan version, omit the Parmesan cheese or use a vegan alternative.

✓ Leftover nettle pesto pasta can be stored in an airtight container in the refrigerator for up to 3 days. Reheat gently on the stovetop or in the microwave before serving.

Nutrition Information (Approximate, per serving):

Calories: 500 Fat: 27g Sodium: 200mg
Carbohydrates: 51g Fiber: 6g Sugars: 2g
Protein: 15g

11

Mushroom and Shrimp Brown Rice Pilaf

Prep Time: 10 minutes

Cook Time: 30 minutes

Servings: 4

Ingredients:

- 3 tbsp olive oil
- 1/4 lb crimini mushrooms, cleaned, stemmed, and diced
- 1/4 lb shrimp, peeled and deveined
- 1 garlic clove, minced
- 1 onion, finely chopped
- 1 2/3 cups long grain brown rice, uncooked
- 4 1/4 cups vegetable broth
- 3 tbsp fresh chives, chopped
- 1/4 lb frozen peas, thawed
- Salt and pepper to taste

Instructions:

1. In a large skillet or saucepan, heat the olive oil over medium heat. Add the diced crimini mushrooms and cook for 5-6 minutes, or until they start to brown and release their moisture.

2. Add the peeled and deveined shrimp to the skillet and cook for 2-3 minutes on each side, or until they turn pink and opaque. Remove the cooked shrimp from the skillet and set aside.

3. In the same skillet, add the minced garlic and finely chopped onion. Cook for 2-3 minutes, or until the onion becomes translucent and aromatic.

4. Add the uncooked long grain brown rice to the skillet and stir to coat it with the oil and flavors. Cook for an additional 2-3 minutes, stirring occasionally, to lightly toast the rice.

5. Pour the vegetable broth into the skillet and bring the mixture to a boil. Reduce the heat to low, cover the skillet with a lid, and simmer for 20-25 minutes, or until the rice is tender and has absorbed the liquid.

6. Once the rice is cooked, fluff it with a fork and stir in the chopped fresh chives and thawed frozen peas. Cook for an additional 2-3 minutes, or until the peas are heated through.

7. Season the mushroom and shrimp brown rice pilaf with salt and pepper to taste.

8. Serve the pilaf hot as a delicious and nutritious main dish or side dish.

Variation and Tips:

✓ Feel free to add other vegetables such as bell peppers, carrots, or spinach for extra flavor and nutrition.

- ✓ Substitute chicken broth or seafood broth for the vegetable broth for a different flavor profile.
- ✓ Garnish the pilaf with additional chopped chives or a sprinkle of grated Parmesan cheese before serving, if desired.
- ✓ Leftover pilaf can be stored in an airtight container in the refrigerator for up to 3 days. Reheat gently on the stovetop or in the microwave before serving. Enjoy your flavorful mushroom and shrimp brown rice pilaf!

Nutrition Information (Approximate, per serving):

Calories: 410 Fat: 12g Sodium: 850mg
Carbohydrates: 60g Fiber: 5g Sugars: 4g

12

Coconut Fish Curry with Brown Rice

Prep Time: 10 minutes

Cook Time: 25 minutes

Servings: 4

Ingredients:

- 1 lb white fish fillet (cod, halibut, or tilapia), cut into bite-sized pieces
- 1 tablespoon olive oil
- 1 onion, chopped
- 2 cloves garlic, minced
- 1 tablespoon curry paste
- 1 can (14 oz) light coconut milk
- 1/2 cup low-sodium chicken broth
- 1/2 cup frozen peas
- Salt and pepper to taste
- 1 cup uncooked brown rice

Instructions:

1. Cook the brown rice according to package instructions until tender and set aside.
2. In a large skillet or saucepan, heat the olive oil over medium heat. Add the chopped onion and minced garlic, and cook for 2-3 minutes until softened and fragrant.
3. Stir in the curry paste and cook for another minute to release its flavors.
4. Add the coconut milk and chicken broth to the skillet, and bring to a gentle simmer.
5. Carefully add the bite-sized fish pieces to the skillet, making sure they are submerged in the sauce. Cook for 5-7 minutes, or until the fish is cooked through and flakes easily with a fork.
6. Add the frozen peas to the skillet and cook for an additional 2-3 minutes, or until heated through.
7. Season the coconut fish curry with salt and pepper to taste.

8. Serve the coconut fish curry over cooked brown rice.

9. Enjoy your flavorful and comforting coconut fish curry with brown rice!

Variation and Tips:

✓ Feel free to use your favorite type of white fish for this recipe, such as cod, halibut, or tilapia.

✓ Customize the level of spice by adjusting the amount of curry paste to suit your taste preferences.

✓ Add additional vegetables such as bell peppers, spinach, or carrots for extra flavor and nutrition.

✓ Garnish with chopped fresh cilantro or a squeeze of lime juice before serving for a burst of freshness.

✓ Leftover coconut fish curry can be stored in an airtight container in the refrigerator for up to 3 days. Reheat gently on the stovetop or in the microwave before serving.

Nutrition Information (Approximate, per serving):

Calories: 380 Fat: 12g Sodium: 250mg Total Carbohydrates: 40g Fiber: 4g Sugars: 3g Protein: 25g

13

Turkey Meatballs in Tomato Sauce

Prep Time: 15 minutes

Cook Time: 25 minutes

Servings: 4

Ingredients:

• 1 pound lean ground turkey

• 1/2 cup finely chopped onion

• 1/2 cup finely chopped mushrooms

• 1/4 cup chopped fresh parsley

• 1/4 cup Italian seasoned breadcrumbs

• 1 egg

• 1/2 teaspoon salt

• 1/4 teaspoon black pepper

• 2 cups tomato sauce

Instructions:

1. Preheat your oven to 375°F (190°C). Lightly grease a baking dish or line it with parchment paper.

2. In a large mixing bowl, combine the ground turkey, chopped onion, chopped mushrooms, chopped parsley, breadcrumbs, egg, salt, and black pepper.

3. Mix well until all ingredients are evenly incorporated.

4. Shape the turkey mixture into meatballs, using about 1-2 tablespoons of mixture for each meatball. Arrange the meatballs in the prepared baking dish.

5. Bake the meatballs in the preheated oven for 20-25 minutes, or until they are cooked through and lightly browned on the outside.

6. While the meatballs are baking, heat the tomato sauce in a saucepan over medium heat until warmed through.

7. Once the meatballs are cooked, remove them from the oven and transfer them to the saucepan with the tomato sauce. Gently stir to coat the meatballs in the sauce.

8. Allow the meatballs to simmer in the sauce for an additional 5-10 minutes, stirring occasionally, to ensure they are heated through and well coated in the sauce.

9. Serve the turkey meatballs hot, either on their own or over cooked pasta or rice, garnished with additional chopped parsley if desired.

10. Enjoy your delicious and flavorful turkey meatballs in tomato sauce!

Variation and Tips:

✓ Feel free to customize the meatball mixture by adding other ingredients such as minced garlic, grated Parmesan cheese, or dried herbs like oregano or basil.

✓ Substitute ground chicken or ground beef for the ground turkey if desired.

✓ Use store-bought tomato sauce or homemade marinara sauce for convenience.

✓ Leftover meatballs and sauce can be stored in an airtight container in the refrigerator for up to 3 days, or frozen for longer storage. Reheat gently on the stovetop or in the microwave before serving.

Nutrition Information (Approximate, per serving):

Calories: 250 Fat 12g Sodium: 500mg Carbohydrates: 20g Fiber 3g Sugars 7g Protein: 25g

14

Roasted Chicken Thighs with Root Vegetables

Prep Time: 15 minutes
Cook Time: 40 minutes
Servings: 4
Ingredients:

- 4 bone-in, skin-on chicken thighs
- 1 tablespoon olive oil
- Salt and pepper to taste

- 1 sweet potato, cut into bite-sized pieces
- 1 parsnip, cut into bite-sized pieces
- 1 turnip, cut into bite-sized pieces
- 1/2 cup low-sodium chicken broth

Instructions:

1. Preheat your oven to 400°F (200°C). Line a baking sheet with parchment paper or foil for easier cleanup.

2. Place the chicken thighs on the prepared baking sheet. Drizzle them with olive oil and season generously with salt and pepper, rubbing the seasoning into the skin.

3. Arrange the sweet potato, parsnip, and turnip pieces around the chicken thighs on the baking sheet. Drizzle the vegetables with a little olive oil and season with salt and pepper.

4. Roast the chicken thighs and vegetables in the preheated oven for 35-40 minutes, or until the chicken is cooked through and the vegetables are tender, with crispy edges.

5. About halfway through the cooking time, carefully remove the baking sheet from the oven and add the chicken broth to the pan, pouring it around the chicken and vegetables. This will help keep the chicken moist and flavorful while adding extra flavor to the vegetables.

6. Return the baking sheet to the oven and continue roasting until the chicken is golden brown and cooked through, and the vegetables are tender and caramelized.

7. Once cooked, remove the baking sheet from the oven and let the chicken thighs rest for a few minutes before serving.

8. Serve the roasted chicken thighs with the caramelized root vegetables, drizzling any pan juices over the top.

9. Enjoy your delicious and comforting roasted chicken thighs with root vegetables!

Variation and Tips:

✓ Feel free to customize the root vegetables based on your preferences or what you have on hand. Other options include carrots, rutabaga, potatoes, or Brussels sprouts.

✓ For added flavor, sprinkle the vegetables with dried herbs such as thyme, rosemary, or sage before roasting.

✓ Serve the roasted chicken thighs and vegetables with a side of cooked quinoa, rice, or couscous for a complete meal.

✓ Leftovers can be stored in an airtight container in the refrigerator for up to 3 days. Reheat gently in the oven or microwave before serving.

Nutrition Information (Approximate, per serving):

Calories: 400 Fat: 20-25g Sodium: 300mg Carbohydrates: 15-20g Fiber: 5g Sugars: 5g Protein: 30g

15

Quinoa Stuffed Bell Peppers

Prep Time: 15 minutes

Cook Time: 30 minutes

Servings: 4

Ingredients:

- 4 bell peppers, halved and seeded
- 1 cup cooked quinoa
- 1 onion, chopped
- 2 cloves garlic, minced
- 1 zucchini, chopped
- 1 cup sliced mushrooms
- 1/4 cup chopped fresh parsley
- 2 tablespoons olive oil
- Salt and pepper to taste

Instructions:

1. Preheat your oven to 375°F (190°C). Lightly grease a baking dish and set aside.

2. In a large skillet, heat olive oil over medium heat. Add chopped onion and minced garlic. Cook until softened and fragrant, about 3-4 minutes.

3. Add chopped zucchini and sliced mushrooms to the skillet. Cook, stirring occasionally, until vegetables are tender, about 5-6 minutes.

4. Stir in cooked quinoa and chopped fresh parsley. Season with salt and pepper to taste. Cook for an additional 2-3 minutes to allow flavors to blend.

5. While the filling is cooking, prepare the bell peppers. Cut each bell pepper in half lengthwise and remove seeds and membranes.

6. Arrange the bell pepper halves in the prepared baking dish. Spoon the quinoa and vegetable mixture evenly into each pepper half.

7. Cover the baking dish with aluminum foil and bake in the preheated oven for 20-25 minutes, or until the peppers are tender.

8. Remove the foil and bake for an additional 5-10 minutes, or until the tops are lightly browned.

9. Once cooked, remove the stuffed bell peppers from the oven and let them cool slightly before serving.

10. Serve the quinoa stuffed bell peppers warm, garnished with additional chopped parsley if desired.

11. Enjoy your nutritious and flavorful quinoa stuffed bell peppers!

Variation and Tips:

✓ Feel free to customize the filling by adding other vegetables or protein sources such as black beans, corn, spinach, or ground turkey.

✓ For a cheesy twist, sprinkle shredded cheese on top of the stuffed peppers during the last few minutes of baking.

✓ Leftover stuffed peppers can be stored in an airtight container in the refrigerator for up to 3 days. Reheat gently in the microwave or oven before serving.

Nutrition Information (Approximate, per serving):

Calories: 250 Protein: 9 g
Carbohydrates: 35g Fat: 12g Fiber: 5g
Sodium: 400mg

16

Turkey and Vegetable Skewers

Prep Time: 15 minutes
Cook Time: 10 minutes
Servings: 4
Ingredients:

- 1 pound turkey breast, cut into cubes
- 1 red bell pepper, cut into chunks
- 1 zucchini, cut into chunks
- 1 onion, cut into chunks
- 2 tablespoons olive oil
- 1 tablespoon chopped fresh herbs (such as thyme, rosemary, or oregano)
- Salt and pepper to taste

Instructions:

1. Preheat your grill or grill pan to medium-high heat.

2. In a bowl, combine the turkey cubes, red bell pepper chunks, zucchini chunks, and onion chunks.

3. Drizzle olive oil over the mixture and sprinkle with chopped fresh herbs. Toss to coat evenly.

4. Season the mixture with salt and pepper according to your taste.

5. Thread the turkey and vegetables onto skewers, alternating between the different ingredients.

6. Place the skewers on the preheated grill and cook for about 8-10 minutes, turning occasionally, until the turkey is cooked through and the vegetables are tender.

7. Once cooked, remove the skewers from the grill and let them rest for a couple of minutes.

8. Serve the turkey and vegetable skewers hot, and enjoy a delicious and healthy meal.

Variation and Tips:

✓ Marinate the turkey in a mixture of olive oil, lemon juice, garlic, and your favorite herbs for added flavor.

✓ Feel free to add cherry tomatoes or mushrooms to the skewers for extra variety.

✓ Serve the skewers with a side of rice, quinoa, or a fresh salad for a complete meal.

✓ If using wooden skewers, remember to soak them in water for about 30 minutes before threading to prevent burning.

Nutrition Information (Approximate, per serving):

Calories: 300 Carbohydrates: 10 g Protein: 35 g Fat: 15 g Fiber: 3 g Sodium: 100 mg

Curried Lentil and Rice Pilaf

Prep Time: 10 minutes

Cook Time: 35-40 minutes

Servings: 4

Ingredients:

- 1 cup brown lentils, rinsed and drained
- 2 cups water
- 1 cup uncooked brown rice
- 2 cups vegetable or chicken stock
- 1 tablespoon curry powder
- 1/2 teaspoon ground cumin
- 1/2 teaspoon ground coriander
- 1/2 cup chopped onion
- 1/2 cup chopped celery
- 1/2 cup chopped bell pepper
- 1/2 cup chopped zucchini
- 1/4 cup chopped cashews
- Salt and pepper to taste

Instructions:

1. In a large pot, combine the rinsed lentils and water. Bring to a boil, then reduce heat, cover, and simmer for 15 minutes.

2. Add the uncooked brown rice and vegetable or chicken stock to the pot with the lentils. Stir in the curry powder, ground cumin, and ground coriander.

3. Cover the pot and simmer for an additional 20-25 minutes, or until the rice and lentils are tender and the liquid is absorbed.

4. While the rice and lentils are cooking, heat a little oil in a skillet over medium heat. Add the chopped onion, celery, bell pepper, and zucchini. Cook until the vegetables are tender, about 5-7 minutes.

5. Once the rice and lentils are cooked, remove the pot from the heat. Stir in the cooked vegetables and chopped cashews. Season with salt and pepper to taste.

6. Serve the curried lentil and rice pilaf hot as a main dish or side dish.

Variation and Tips:

✓ Feel free to add other vegetables of your choice, such as carrots, peas, or spinach.

✓ For extra flavor, you can add minced garlic and grated ginger to the vegetable mixture.

✓ Garnish with fresh cilantro or chopped green onions before serving.

✓ This dish can be made ahead of time and stored in the refrigerator for up to 3 days. Reheat before serving.

Nutrition Information (Approximate, per serving):

Calories: 350 Carbohydrates: 61 g Protein: 16 g Fat: 5 g Fiber: 12 g Sodium: 600 mg

18

Roasted Chicken Thighs with Root Vegetables

Prep Time: 10 minutes

Cook Time: 40-45 minutes

Servings: 4

Ingredients:

- 4 bone-in, skin-on chicken thighs
- 1 tablespoon olive oil
- Salt and pepper to taste
- 1 sweet potato, cut into bite-sized pieces
- 1 parsnip, cut into bite-sized pieces
- 1 turnip, cut into bite-sized pieces
- 1/2 cup vegetable or chicken stock

Instructions:

1. Preheat the oven to 400°F (200°C).

2. Place the chicken thighs on a baking sheet lined with parchment paper or aluminum foil. Drizzle with olive oil and season with salt and pepper.

3. In a large bowl, toss the sweet potato, parsnip, and turnip with olive oil, salt, and pepper until evenly coated.

4. Arrange the vegetables around the chicken thighs on the baking sheet.

5. Pour the vegetable or chicken stock over the vegetables.

6. Roast in the preheated oven for 40-45 minutes, or until the chicken is cooked through and the vegetables are tender, turning the vegetables halfway through cooking.

7. Remove from the oven and let rest for a few minutes before serving.

8. Serve the roasted chicken thighs with root vegetables hot, garnished with fresh herbs if desired.

Variation and Tips:

✓ Feel free to add other root vegetables such as carrots or rutabaga to the mix.

✓ You can season the chicken thighs with your favorite herbs and spices for added flavor.

✓ For a crispy skin, you can broil the chicken thighs for a few minutes at the end of cooking.

✓ Serve with a side of steamed greens or a simple salad for a complete meal.

Nutrition Information (Approximate, per serving):

Calories: 350 Carbohydrates: 20 g Protein: 25 g Fat: 18 g Fiber: 5 g Sodium: 300 mg

19

Baked White Fish with Vegetables

Prep Time: 10 minutes

Cook Time: 20-25 minutes

Servings: 4

Ingredients:

- 1 lb white fish fillet (such as tilapia or halibut), cut into bite-sized pieces
- 1 red bell pepper, sliced
- 1 zucchini, sliced
- 1 cup cherry tomatoes
- 1/4 cup chopped red onion
- 2 tablespoons olive oil
- 1 tablespoon dried dill
- 1/2 teaspoon salt
- 1/4 teaspoon black pepper

Instructions:

1. Preheat the oven to 375°F (190°C).

2. In a large bowl, combine the white fish pieces, sliced red bell pepper,

zucchini slices, cherry tomatoes, and chopped red onion.

3. Drizzle olive oil over the mixture and sprinkle with dried dill, salt, and black pepper. Toss until the ingredients are evenly coated.

4. Transfer the seasoned fish and vegetables to a baking dish or sheet pan lined with parchment paper.

5. Bake in the preheated oven for 20-25 minutes, or until the fish is cooked through and the vegetables are tender.

6. Once cooked, remove from the oven and let it rest for a few minutes.

7. Serve the baked white fish and vegetables hot, garnished with fresh herbs if desired.

Variation and Tips:

✓ Feel free to use any white fish fillet of your choice, such as cod or haddock.

✓ Add additional vegetables like sliced mushrooms or asparagus for extra flavor and nutrition.

✓ Experiment with different herbs and spices to customize the flavor of the dish.

✓ Serve with a side of cooked quinoa or brown rice for a complete meal.

Nutrition Information (Approximate, per serving):

Calories: 220 Carbohydrates: 10 g Protein: 25 g Fat: 10 g Fiber: 3 g Sodium: 350 mg

20

Stir-Fried Shrimp with Mixed Vegetables

Prep Time: 10 minutes

Cook Time: 10-15 minutes

Servings: 4

Ingredients:

• 1 pound shrimp, peeled and deveined

• 2 cups mixed vegetables (such as snow peas, bell peppers, and carrots)

• 1 onion, chopped

• 2 cloves garlic, minced

• 2 tablespoons low-sodium soy sauce

• 1 tablespoon olive oil

• Salt and pepper to taste

Instructions:

1. Heat olive oil in a large skillet or wok over medium-high heat.

2. Add chopped onion and minced garlic to the skillet. Stir-fry for 2-3 minutes until fragrant and onions are translucent.

3. Add the mixed vegetables to the skillet. Stir-fry for 4-5 minutes until they are crisp-tender.

4. Push the vegetables to one side of the skillet and add the shrimp to the empty space. Cook for 2-3 minutes on each side until they turn pink and opaque.

5. Combine the shrimp with the cooked vegetables in the skillet.

6. Pour low-sodium soy sauce over the shrimp and vegetables. Stir well to coat everything evenly.

7. Season with salt and pepper to taste.

8. Cook for an additional 1-2 minutes, stirring constantly, until the shrimp and vegetables are heated through.

9. Remove from heat and serve the stir-fried shrimp and mixed vegetables hot over cooked rice or noodles.

Variation and Tips:

✓ Feel free to add other vegetables like broccoli, snap peas, or mushrooms to the stir-fry for extra flavor and nutrients.

✓ Customize the seasoning by adding minced ginger, red pepper flakes, or sesame oil for additional depth of flavor.

✓ Serve with a sprinkle of sesame seeds or chopped green onions for garnish.

✓ Adjust the soy sauce quantity according to your taste preference, keeping in mind the saltiness of the sauce.

Nutrition Information (Approximate, per serving):

Calories: 250 Carbohydrates: 14 g Protein: 30 g Fat: 8 g Fiber: 4 g Sodium: 500 mg

SOUPS

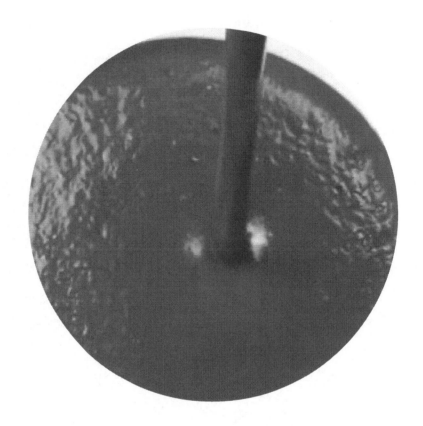

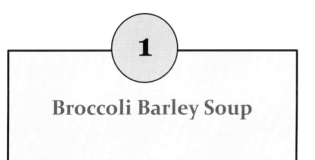

Broccoli Barley Soup

Prep Time: 15 minutes

Cook Time: 25 minutes

Servings: 4

Ingredients:

- 1/4 cup yellow onion, chopped
- 1 small carrot, peeled and diced
- 1 rib organic celery, finely chopped
- 1 tablespoon extra-virgin olive oil
- 4 cups small, organic broccoli florets
- 1/2 cup pearled barley, cooked
- 5 cups vegetable broth
- 1 can (14 1/2 oz) stewed tomatoes
- 4 cloves garlic, minced
- 1/4 teaspoon dried marjoram
- 1 teaspoon thyme
- Salt and pepper, to taste

Instructions:

1. In a large pot, heat the olive oil over medium heat. Add the chopped onion, diced carrot, and finely chopped celery. Cook for about 5 minutes until the vegetables begin to soften.

2. Add the minced garlic to the pot and cook for an additional 1-2 minutes until fragrant.

3. Pour in the vegetable broth and stewed tomatoes (including their juices) into the pot. Stir well to combine.

4. Add the broccoli florets, cooked pearled barley, dried marjoram, and thyme to the pot. Season with salt and pepper to taste.

5. Bring the soup to a boil, then reduce the heat to low and let it simmer for about 15-20 minutes until the vegetables are tender.

6. Taste and adjust seasoning if necessary. Serve the broccoli barley soup hot, garnished with fresh herbs if desired.

Variation and Tips:

✓ Feel free to customize the soup by adding other vegetables such as chopped spinach, kale, or bell peppers.

✓ Substitute the pearled barley with cooked brown rice or quinoa for a gluten-free option.

✓ For a creamier texture, use an immersion blender to partially blend the soup while still leaving some chunky vegetables.

✓ Store any leftover soup in an airtight container in the refrigerator for up to 3-4 days, or freeze for longer storage.

Nutrition Information (Approximate, per serving):

Calories: 200 Protein: 6g Carbohydrates: 30g Fiber: 10g Sugars: 8 g Fat: 8g Sodium: 700mg

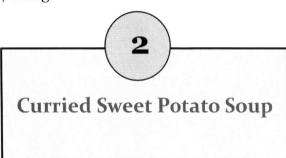

2

Curried Sweet Potato Soup

Prep Time: 10 minutes

Cook Time: 25 minutes

Servings: 4

Ingredients:

- 1 tablespoon canola oil
- 1 large yellow onion, coarsely chopped
- 1 clove garlic, smashed
- 2 teaspoons curry powder
- 1 1/2 pounds sweet potatoes (pink, orange, or yellow variety), peeled and chopped
- 1/2 inch piece fresh ginger, peeled and finely chopped
- 3 cups low-sodium vegetable broth
- Chopped parsley, for garnish

Instructions:

1. In a large pot, heat the canola oil over medium heat. Add the chopped onion and smashed garlic clove. Cook for about 5 minutes until the onion is softened.

2. Stir in the curry powder and cook for another minute until fragrant.

3. Add the chopped sweet potatoes and finely chopped ginger to the pot. Stir to coat the sweet potatoes with the curry mixture.

4. Pour in the vegetable broth, ensuring that the sweet potatoes are fully submerged. Bring the mixture to a boil.

5. Once boiling, reduce the heat to low, cover the pot, and let the soup simmer for about 15-20 minutes until the sweet potatoes are tender.

6. Remove the pot from the heat and let the soup cool slightly.

7. Using an immersion blender or regular blender, puree the soup until smooth and creamy.

8. Return the soup to the pot and reheat if necessary.

9. Serve the curried sweet potato soup hot, garnished with chopped parsley.

Variation and Tips:

✓ For added creaminess, stir in a splash of coconut milk before serving.

✓ Adjust the amount of curry powder according to your taste preferences for a milder or spicier soup.

✓ Garnish with a dollop of Greek yogurt or sour cream for extra richness.

✓ Serve the soup with crusty bread or naan for a satisfying meal.

Nutrition Information (Approximate, per serving):

Calories: 200- Protein: 6g Carbohydrates: 40g Fiber: 6g Sugars: 10g Fat: 7g Sodium: 400 mg

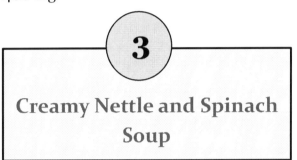

Creamy Nettle and Spinach Soup

Prep Time: 10 minutes

Cook Time: 20 minutes

Servings: 4

Ingredients:

- 6 ounces young nettle tips
- 4 ounces fresh spinach
- 2 tablespoons olive oil
- 2 shallots, chopped
- 2 cups water
- 2 cups skimmed organic milk
- 3 tablespoons flour
- Dash of ground white pepper
- Dash of ground nutmeg
- Salt to taste
- Yoghurt with probiotic bacteria, for garnish

Instructions:

1. Begin by thoroughly washing the nettle tips and spinach under cold water. Drain and set aside.

2. In a large pot, heat the olive oil over medium heat. Add the chopped shallots and sauté until they become translucent.

3. Add the washed nettle tips and spinach to the pot. Stir and cook for about 5 minutes until they wilt and reduce in volume.

4. In a separate bowl, whisk together the water, skimmed organic milk, and flour until smooth.

5. Slowly pour the milk mixture into the pot while stirring continuously to prevent lumps from forming.

6. Season the soup with a dash of ground white pepper, ground nutmeg, and salt to taste.

7. Allow the soup to simmer gently for about 10 minutes, stirring occasionally, until it thickens slightly.

8. Once the soup reaches your desired consistency and the flavors have melded together, remove it from the heat.

9. Serve the creamy nettle and spinach soup hot, garnished with a dollop of yoghurt with probiotic bacteria for added creaminess.

Variation and Tips:

✓ For extra richness, you can substitute part of the skimmed organic milk with heavy cream.

✓ Feel free to adjust the seasoning according to your taste preferences by adding more salt, pepper, or nutmeg.

✓ If you prefer a smoother texture, you can use an immersion blender to puree the soup until creamy.

✓ Serve the soup with crusty bread or garlic croutons for a satisfying meal.

Nutrition Information (Approximate, per serving):

Calories: 150 Protein: 10g Carbohydrates: 15g Fiber: 5g Sugars: 6g Fat: 7-9 g Sodium: 400 mg

4

Pea and Watercress Soup

Prep Time: 10 minutes

Cook Time: 20 minutes

Servings: 4

Ingredients:

- 1 large onion
- 1 garlic clove
- 6 cups vegetable or chicken stock
- 1 zucchini
- 30 oz frozen peas

- 3 oz watercress
- Salt and pepper, to taste

Instructions:

1. Start by finely chopping the large onion and mincing the garlic clove.

2. In a large pot, heat some olive oil over medium heat. Add the chopped onion and minced garlic, and sauté until softened and fragrant.

3. Pour in the vegetable or chicken stock and bring it to a gentle simmer.

4. While the stock is heating, chop the zucchini into small pieces.

5. Add the chopped zucchini and frozen peas to the pot. Stir well and allow them to cook for about 5-7 minutes until tender.

6. Once the peas and zucchini are cooked through, add the watercress to the pot. Stir to combine.

7. Let the soup simmer for another 2-3 minutes until the watercress wilts and blends into the soup.

8. Season the soup with salt and pepper to taste, adjusting the seasoning as needed.

9. Remove the soup from the heat and allow it to cool slightly before serving.

10. Ladle the pea and watercress soup into bowls and garnish with additional watercress leaves if desired.

Variation and Tips:

✓ For added creaminess, you can blend the soup using an immersion blender until smooth.

✓ Serve the soup with a dollop of Greek yogurt or a swirl of heavy cream for extra richness.

✓ Feel free to customize the soup by adding other vegetables such as carrots, celery, or leeks.

✓ Garnish the soup with a sprinkle of fresh herbs like chopped chives or parsley for a burst of flavor.

Nutrition Information (Approximate, per serving):

Calories: 150 Protein: 10g Carbohydrates: 25 g Fiber: 10 g Sugars: 8 g Fat: 5 g Sodium: 600mg

5

Garlic and Tomato Soup

Prep Time: 10 minutes

Cook Time: 20 minutes

Servings: 4

Ingredients:

• 3 large garlic cloves

• 3 oz shallots, peeled and sliced

• 1 tablespoon olive oil

• 1 (14 1/2-ounce) can stewed tomatoes, undrained

• 1 1/2 cups chicken broth

• 1/2 teaspoon apple cider vinegar

• 1/4 teaspoon salt

• Dash of freshly ground red pepper

• 2 tablespoons fresh basil, chopped

Instructions:

1. Begin by mincing the large garlic cloves.

2. In a large pot, heat the olive oil over medium heat. Add the minced garlic and sliced shallots, and sauté until softened and fragrant.

3. Pour in the stewed tomatoes with their juices and the chicken broth. Stir well to combine.

4. Bring the mixture to a gentle simmer, then reduce the heat and let it cook for about 10-15 minutes to allow the flavors to meld together.

5. Once the soup has simmered and the flavors have developed, remove the pot from the heat.

6. Using an immersion blender or a regular blender, carefully puree the soup until smooth and creamy.

7. Return the soup to the pot and place it back over low heat.

8. Stir in the apple cider vinegar, salt, and a dash of freshly ground red pepper. Adjust the seasoning to taste.

9. Let the soup simmer for another 5 minutes to allow the flavors to blend.

10. Just before serving, stir in the chopped fresh basil.

11. Ladle the garlic and tomato soup into bowls and garnish with additional fresh basil leaves if desired.

Variation and Tips:

✓ For a richer flavor, you can roast the garlic cloves in the oven before adding them to the soup.

✓ If you prefer a smoother texture, you can strain the soup through a fine mesh sieve after blending to remove any remaining solids.

✓ Serve the soup with a dollop of Greek yogurt or a sprinkle of grated Parmesan cheese for added creaminess.

✓ Feel free to customize the soup by adding other herbs and spices such as oregano, thyme, or paprika.

✓ Garnish the soup with a drizzle of olive oil or a swirl of balsamic glaze for an extra touch of flavor.

Nutrition Information (Approximate, per serving):

Calories: 80 Protein: 2g Carbohydrates: 10g Fiber: 3g Sugars: 5 g Fat: 5g Sodium: 500mg

6

Beet and Carrot Soup

Prep Time: 15 minutes

Cook Time: 30 minutes

Servings: 6

Ingredients:

- 3 medium beets, peeled and diced
- 1 tbsp olive oil
- 1 cup onion, chopped
- 1 pound carrots, diced
- 1 tbsp fresh ginger, minced
- 1 garlic clove, minced
- 6 cups vegetable stock

Instructions:

1. Heat olive oil in a large pot over medium heat.

2. Add chopped onion and sauté until translucent, about 5 minutes.

3. Add minced garlic and ginger, and cook for another 1-2 minutes until fragrant.

4. Add diced beets and carrots to the pot, and cook for 5 minutes, stirring occasionally.

5. Pour in the vegetable stock and bring the mixture to a boil.

6. Reduce heat to low, cover the pot, and let the soup simmer for about 20-25

minutes, or until the vegetables are tender.

7. Once the vegetables are cooked through, remove the pot from the heat.

8. Using an immersion blender or a regular blender, carefully puree the soup until smooth and creamy.

9. If the soup is too thick, you can add more vegetable stock or water to reach your desired consistency.

10. Taste the soup and adjust seasoning with salt and pepper as needed.

11. Serve the beet and carrot soup hot, garnished with fresh herbs or a dollop of yogurt if desired.

Variation and Tips:

✓ For added creaminess, stir in a splash of coconut milk or heavy cream before serving.

✓ Garnish with a sprinkle of chopped fresh parsley, cilantro, or chives for extra flavor and color.

✓ Add a squeeze of lemon juice or a splash of apple cider vinegar for a tangy kick.

✓ Customize the soup by adding other vegetables like potatoes, celery, or parsnips.

✓ For a smoother texture, strain the soup through a fine mesh sieve after blending.

✓ Store any leftovers in an airtight container in the refrigerator for up to 4-5 days or freeze for longer storage.

Nutrition Information (Approximate, per serving):

Calories: 120 Protein: 2g Carbohydrates: 25g Fiber: 6g Sugars: 12 g Fat: 3-5 g Sodium: 700 mg

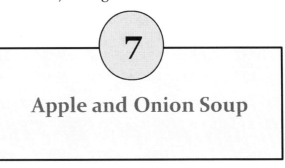

7

Apple and Onion Soup

Prep Time: 15 minutes

Cook Time: 30 minutes

Servings: 4-6

Ingredients:

- 1 Tbsp canola oil
- 2 medium yellow onions, sliced
- 1 small leek, chopped
- 1/2 Tbsp fresh rosemary, chopped
- 1/2 Tbsp fresh thyme
- 3 organic apples, cut into small dices
- 6 cups fat-free, low-sodium vegetable broth

Instructions:

1. Heat canola oil in a large pot over medium heat.

2. Add sliced onions and chopped leek to the pot. Cook, stirring occasionally,

until the onions are soft and translucent, about 5-7 minutes.

3. Stir in the chopped rosemary and thyme, and cook for another 1-2 minutes until fragrant.

4. Add the diced apples to the pot and cook for 3-4 minutes, stirring occasionally.

5. Pour in the vegetable broth and bring the mixture to a boil.

6. Reduce heat to low, cover the pot, and let the soup simmer for about 20-25 minutes, or until the apples are tender.

7. Once the apples are cooked through, remove the pot from the heat.

8. Using an immersion blender or a regular blender, carefully puree the soup until smooth and creamy.

9. If the soup is too thick, you can add more vegetable broth or water to reach your desired consistency.

10. Taste the soup and adjust seasoning with salt and pepper as needed.

11. Serve the apple and onion soup hot, garnished with a sprinkle of chopped fresh herbs if desired.

Variation and Tips:

✓ For added richness, stir in a splash of coconut milk or heavy cream before serving.

✓ Garnish with a drizzle of balsamic glaze or a dollop of yogurt for extra flavor.

✓ Add a pinch of nutmeg or cinnamon for a hint of warmth and spice.

✓ Customize the soup by adding other vegetables like carrots, celery, or potatoes.

✓ For a smoother texture, strain the soup through a fine mesh sieve after blending.

✓ Store any leftovers in an airtight container in the refrigerator for up to 4-5 days or freeze for longer storage.

Nutrition Information (Approximate, per serving):

Calories: 120 Protein: 3 g Carbohydrates: 20g Fiber: 6 g Sugars: 12 g Fat: 5 Sodium: 700mg

8

Chicken and Vegetable Soup

Prep Time: 15 minutes

Cook Time: 30 minutes

Servings: 4-6

Ingredients:

• 4 cups fat-free, low-sodium chicken broth

• 1 onion, chopped

- 3/4 cup sweet potato, diced
- 3/4 cup turnip, diced
- 2 ribs organic celery, diced
- 2 carrots, sliced
- 1/2 cup fresh parsley, chopped
- 2 cups skinless, organic chicken, cooked and diced

Instructions:

1. In a large pot, bring the chicken broth to a simmer over medium heat.
2. Add the chopped onion, diced sweet potato, turnip, celery, and carrots to the pot.
3. Allow the vegetables to cook in the simmering broth for about 15-20 minutes, or until they are tender.
4. Once the vegetables are cooked through, add the diced chicken to the pot.
5. Continue to simmer the soup for an additional 5-10 minutes, allowing the flavors to meld together.
6. Stir in the chopped parsley and season the soup with salt and pepper to taste.
7. Serve the chicken and vegetable soup hot, garnished with additional parsley if desired.

Variation and Tips:

✓ Feel free to add other vegetables such as diced potatoes, green beans, or peas for added nutrition and flavor.
✓ For a heartier soup, you can add cooked pasta or rice.
✓ Customize the soup by adding your favorite herbs and spices such as thyme, rosemary, or garlic powder.
✓ If you prefer a thicker soup, you can mash some of the cooked vegetables with a fork or potato masher before adding the chicken.
✓ Store any leftovers in an airtight container in the refrigerator for up to 3-4 days or freeze for longer storage.

Nutrition Information (Approximate, per serving):

Calories: 150 Protein: 15g Carbohydrates: 15 g Fiber: 5 g Sugars: 6 g Fat: 5 g Sodium: 600 mg

9

Miso Soup with Tofu and Wakame

Prep Time: 10 minutes

Cook Time: 15 minutes

Servings: 4

Ingredients:

- 4 cups low-sodium vegetable broth
- 4 tablespoons white miso paste
- 8 ounces firm tofu, cut into small cubes
- 2 green onions, thinly sliced

- 1/4 cup wakame seaweed, rehydrated in water and drained

Instructions:

1. In a medium pot, bring the vegetable broth to a gentle simmer over medium heat.

2. In a small bowl, whisk together the miso paste with a few tablespoons of warm water until smooth.

3. Add the diluted miso paste to the simmering broth and stir well to combine.

4. Add the cubed tofu to the soup and let it simmer for about 5-7 minutes, allowing the flavors to meld together.

5. Stir in the sliced green onions and rehydrated wakame seaweed.

6. Cook the soup for another 2-3 minutes until the tofu is heated through and the green onions are tender.

7. Taste the soup and adjust the seasoning if necessary, adding more miso paste for saltiness if desired.

8. Serve the miso soup hot, garnished with additional sliced green onions if desired.

Variation and Tips:

✓ Feel free to add other vegetables such as sliced mushrooms, bok choy, or spinach for added nutrition and flavor.

✓ For a heartier soup, you can add cooked soba noodles or rice noodles.

✓ Customize the soup by adding a splash of soy sauce or sesame oil for extra flavor.

✓ If you prefer a smoother texture, you can blend the soup with an immersion blender before adding the tofu and seaweed.

✓ Store any leftovers in an airtight container in the refrigerator for up to 3-4 days.

Nutrition Information (Approximate, per serving):

Calories: 100 Protein: 10 g
Carbohydrates: 10 g Fiber: 3 g Sugars: 3 g
Fat: 6 g Sodium: 600 mg

10

Butternut Squash Soup

Prep Time: 15 minutes
Cook Time: 30 minutes
Servings: 4-6
Ingredients:

- 1 large butternut squash, peeled, seeded, and cut into chunks
- 1 onion, chopped
- 2 cloves garlic, minced
- 4 cups low-sodium vegetable broth
- 1 teaspoon ground cinnamon
- 1/2 teaspoon ground nutmeg

- Salt and pepper to taste

Instructions:

1. In a large pot, heat a little olive oil over medium heat. Add the chopped onion and minced garlic, and sauté until softened and fragrant.

2. Add the butternut squash chunks to the pot and cook for a few minutes, stirring occasionally.

3. Pour in the vegetable broth, making sure it covers the squash and onions. Bring the mixture to a boil.

4. Reduce the heat to low, cover the pot, and let the soup simmer for about 20-25 minutes, or until the squash is tender.

5. Once the squash is cooked through, use an immersion blender to purée the soup until smooth. Alternatively, transfer the soup in batches to a blender and blend until smooth, then return it to the pot.

6. Stir in the ground cinnamon and nutmeg, and season with salt and pepper to taste. Adjust the seasoning if necessary.

7. Allow the soup to simmer for another 5-10 minutes to let the flavors meld together.

8. Serve the butternut squash soup hot, garnished with a sprinkle of fresh herbs or a drizzle of coconut cream, if desired.

Variation and Tips:

✓ For added creaminess, you can stir in a little coconut milk or heavy cream just before serving.

✓ Customize the soup by adding other spices such as cumin, ginger, or curry powder for different flavor profiles.

✓ You can roast the butternut squash chunks in the oven before adding them to the soup for a richer flavor.

✓ Garnish each serving with a dollop of Greek yogurt or sour cream for a tangy contrast.

✓ Store any leftovers in an airtight container in the refrigerator for up to 3-4 days, or freeze for longer storage.

Nutrition Information (Approximate, per serving):

Calories: 120 Protein: 2g Carbohydrates: 30 g Fiber: 7 g Sugars: 8 g Fat: 2 g Sodium: 400 mg

DESSERTS

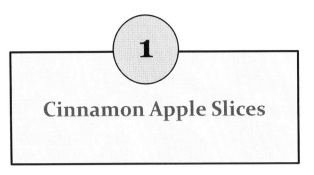

Cinnamon Apple Slices

Prep Time: 5 minutes

Cook Time: 0 minutes

Servings: 1

Ingredients:

- 1 medium apple, cored and sliced
- 1/4 tsp ground cinnamon

Instructions:

1. Wash the apple thoroughly under running water. Use a sharp knife or an apple corer to remove the core, then slice the apple into thin slices.

2. Place the apple slices in a bowl or on a serving plate.

3. Sprinkle the ground cinnamon evenly over the apple slices.

4. Gently toss the apple slices to ensure they are evenly coated with the cinnamon.

5. Serve immediately as a healthy snack or dessert option.

Variation and Tips:

✓ You can adjust the amount of cinnamon according to your taste preferences. Some people prefer a stronger cinnamon flavor, while others may prefer a lighter touch.

✓ For added sweetness, you can drizzle a little honey or maple syrup over the apple slices before sprinkling them with cinnamon.

✓ Experiment with different apple varieties to find your favorite combination. Some popular options include Gala, Fuji, Honeycrisp, and Granny Smith apples.

✓ If you'd like to add a bit of crunch to the dish, sprinkle some chopped nuts or granola over the cinnamon-coated apple slices.

✓ These cinnamon apple slices are delicious on their own, but you can also serve them with a dollop of Greek yogurt or a scoop of vanilla ice cream for a more indulgent treat.

Nutrition Information (Approximate, per serving):

Calories: 50 Carbohydrates: 13 g Fiber: 2.5 g Sugars: 9 g Fat: 0.3 g Protein: 0.3 g Sodium: 0 mg

Mango Green Tea Smoothie

Prep Time: 10 minutes

Cook Time: 0 minutes

Servings: 2

Ingredients:

- 2 cups mango, peeled and chopped
- 1 cup green tea made from loose leaves
- 1 Tbsp honey
- 1/2 inch piece fresh ginger, peeled and finely chopped
- 1 cup crushed ice

Instructions:

1. Brew one cup of green tea using loose leaves and let it cool to room temperature.
2. In a blender, combine the chopped mango, cooled green tea, honey, finely chopped ginger, and crushed ice.
3. Blend all the ingredients until smooth and creamy.
4. Taste the smoothie and adjust the sweetness by adding more honey if desired.
5. Once blended to your liking, pour the smoothie into glasses and serve immediately.

Variation and Tips:

- ✓ You can use frozen mango chunks instead of fresh mango for a colder and thicker smoothie.
- ✓ For added creaminess, you can incorporate yogurt or coconut milk into the smoothie.
- ✓ Experiment with different sweeteners such as agave syrup or maple syrup if you prefer alternatives to honey.
- ✓ If you're a fan of extra spice, you can increase the amount of fresh ginger for a stronger ginger kick.
- ✓ Garnish the smoothie with a slice of fresh mango or a sprig of mint for a decorative touch.

Nutrition Information (Approximate, per serving):

Calories: 150 Carbohydrates: 37 g Fiber: 3g Sugars: 32 g Fat: 0.5 g Protein: 1 g Sodium: 5 mg

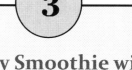

3

Berry Smoothie with Flaxseed

Prep Time: 10 minutes

Cook Time: 0 minutes

Servings: 2

Ingredients:

- 1 cup fresh raspberries
- 1 cup wild blueberries
- 3/4 cup rice milk
- 3/4 cup crushed ice
- 1 Tbsp flaxseed, freshly ground

Instructions:

1. In a blender, combine the fresh raspberries, wild blueberries, rice milk, crushed ice, and freshly ground flaxseed.

2. Blend all the ingredients until smooth and creamy.

3. Taste the smoothie and adjust the sweetness or thickness by adding more fruit or ice as desired.

4. Once blended to your liking, pour the smoothie into glasses and serve immediately.

Variation and Tips:

✓ Feel free to swap rice milk with any other type of milk you prefer, such as almond milk, soy milk, or coconut milk.

✓ You can add a banana to the smoothie for extra creaminess and sweetness.

✓ Experiment with different combinations of berries, such as strawberries, blackberries, or mixed berries.

✓ If you prefer a sweeter smoothie, you can add a drizzle of honey or maple syrup.

✓ For an extra nutritional boost, you can add a handful of spinach or kale to the smoothie without affecting the taste.

Nutrition Information (Approximate, per serving):

Calories: 120 Carbohydrates: 22 g Fiber: 8g Sugars: 10 g Fat: 3 g Protein: 2 g Sodium: 30 mg

Gluten-Free Carrot Muffins

Prep Time: 15 minutes

Cook Time: 20 minutes

Servings: 12 muffins

Ingredients:

- 1 egg
- 1 cup rice milk
- 4 tbsp canola oil
- 2 cups quinoa flour or other gluten-free flour
- 1 tsp guar gum
- 1 tbsp flaxseed meal
- 3 1/2 tsp gluten-free baking powder
- 1/2 tsp salt
- 1 tsp cinnamon
- 1/4 cup brown sugar
- 1 cup organic carrots, grated
- 1/4 cup raisins

Instructions:

1. Preheat the oven to 375°F (190°C). Grease a muffin tin or line with paper liners.

2. In a large mixing bowl, beat the egg. Add rice milk and canola oil, then mix well.

3. In a separate bowl, combine the quinoa flour, guar gum, flaxseed meal,

baking powder, salt, cinnamon, and brown sugar.

4. Gradually add the dry ingredients to the wet ingredients, stirring until just combined.

5. Fold in the grated carrots and raisins until evenly distributed throughout the batter.

6. Spoon the batter into the prepared muffin tin, filling each cup about 2/3 full.

7. Bake in the preheated oven for 18-20 minutes, or until a toothpick inserted into the center of a muffin comes out clean.

8. Allow the muffins to cool in the tin for a few minutes, then transfer them to a wire rack to cool completely.

Variation and Tips:

✓ You can add chopped nuts, such as walnuts or pecans, for added texture and flavor.

✓ Substitute other dried fruits, such as chopped dates or cranberries, for the raisins if desired.

✓ Feel free to adjust the amount of cinnamon and brown sugar to suit your taste preferences.

✓ These muffins freeze well, so you can store any leftovers in an airtight container in the freezer for future enjoyment.

Nutrition Information (Approximate, per serving):

Calories: 190 Carbohydrates: 27 g Fiber: 2g Sugars: 6 g Fat: 8 g Protein: 3 g Sodium: 200 mg

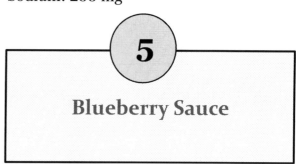

5

Blueberry Sauce

Prep Time: 5 minutes

Cook Time: 10 minutes

Servings: Makes about 2 cups of sauce

Ingredients:

- 4 cups blueberries
- 2 cups water
- 1/2 cup sugar
- 4 tbsp potato starch

Instructions:

1. In a saucepan, combine the blueberries and water. Bring to a boil over medium heat.

2. Reduce the heat to low and simmer the blueberries for about 5 minutes, until they begin to break down and release their juices.

3. In a small bowl, mix the potato starch with a little water to create a slurry.

4. Stir the sugar into the simmering blueberries until dissolved.

5. Slowly pour the potato starch slurry into the blueberry mixture, stirring constantly.

6. Continue to simmer the sauce for another 2-3 minutes, stirring frequently, until it thickens to your desired consistency.

7. Remove the saucepan from the heat and let the blueberry sauce cool slightly before serving.

Variation and Tips:

✓ For a smoother sauce, you can blend the cooked blueberries with an immersion blender or food processor before adding the potato starch slurry.

✓ Adjust the amount of sugar to taste, depending on the sweetness of your blueberries.

✓ This blueberry sauce is delicious served warm over pancakes, waffles, ice cream, or yogurt. You can also use it as a topping for cakes or pies.

✓ Store any leftover sauce in an airtight container in the refrigerator for up to a week.

Nutrition Information (Approximate, per serving):

Calories: 80 Carbohydrates: 20 g Sugars: 15 g Fat: 0 g Protein: 0 g Sodium: 0 mg

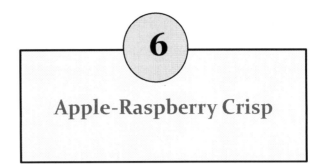

6

Apple-Raspberry Crisp

Prep Time: 15 minutes

Cook Time: 30 minutes

Servings: 6

Ingredients:

• 5 large cooking apples, finely sliced

• 1 cup raspberries

• 2 cups apple juice

• 2 cups rolled oats

• 2 tbsp butter or margarine

• 2 tbsp brown sugar

• 2 tsp cinnamon

• 1/2 tsp cloves

Instructions:

Preheat your oven to 350°F (175°C).

1. In a large mixing bowl, combine the sliced apples and raspberries.

2. Pour the apple juice over the fruit mixture and toss gently to coat.

3. In a separate bowl, combine the rolled oats, brown sugar, cinnamon, and cloves.

4. Cut in the butter or margarine until the mixture resembles coarse crumbs.

5. Spread the fruit mixture evenly into a baking dish.

6. Sprinkle the oat mixture over the fruit, covering it completely.

7. Bake in the preheated oven for 25-30 minutes, or until the topping is golden brown and the fruit is tender.

8. Remove from the oven and let cool slightly before serving.

Variation and Tips:

✓ Feel free to use your favorite combination of fruits for this crisp. Pears, peaches, or blackberries would also work well.

✓ Serve the apple-raspberry crisp warm with a scoop of vanilla ice cream or a dollop of whipped cream for an extra special treat.

✓ You can make this dessert ahead of time and reheat it in the oven before serving.

✓ Experiment with different spices in the oat topping, such as nutmeg or ginger, for added flavor.

Nutrition Information (Approximate, per serving):

Calories: 300 Carbohydrates: 55 g Sugars: 30 g Fat: 6 g Protein: 5 g Fiber: 8 g Sodium: 50 mg

7

Nettle Pancakes with Raspberry Sauce

Prep Time: 15 minutes

Cook Time: 20 minutes

Servings: 8-10 pancakes

Ingredients:

- 2 organic eggs
- 2 cups organic milk
- 1 cup all-purpose flour
- 7 oz young nettle shoots, blanched and chopped
- 1/4 tsp white pepper
- Pinch of salt
- Vegetable cooking spray
- Fresh raspberries, mashed

Instructions:

1. In a large mixing bowl, whisk together the eggs and milk until well combined.

2. Gradually add the flour to the egg and milk mixture, stirring continuously until a smooth batter forms.

3. Stir in the chopped nettle shoots, white pepper, and a pinch of salt until evenly distributed throughout the batter.

4. Heat a non-stick skillet or griddle over medium heat and lightly coat with vegetable cooking spray.

5. Pour a ladleful of the batter onto the hot skillet, spreading it out slightly into a round shape.

6. Cook the pancake for 2-3 minutes on each side, or until golden brown and cooked through.

7. Repeat with the remaining batter, cooking additional pancakes as needed.

8. Serve the nettle pancakes warm, topped with mashed fresh raspberries.

Variations and Tips:

✓ Feel free to adjust the amount of nettle shoots according to your preference.

✓ Substitute the raspberries with your favorite fruit sauce or compote.

✓ These pancakes can also be served with maple syrup, honey, or yogurt for added sweetness.

✓ To make the raspberry sauce, simply mash fresh raspberries with a fork until smooth. You can strain the mixture if you prefer a smoother consistency.

Nutrition Information (Approximate, per serving):

Calories: 120 Carbohydrates: 16 g Sugars: 3 g Fat: 4 g Protein: 6 g Fiber: 1 g Sodium: 120 mg

8

Apple Raspberry Crisp

Prep Time: 15 minutes

Cook Time: 40-45 minutes

Servings: 6

Ingredients:

- 5 large cooking apples, finely sliced
- 1 cup raspberries
- 2 cups apple juice
- 2 cups rolled oats
- 2 tbsp butter or margarine
- 2 tbsp brown sugar
- 2 tsp cinnamon
- 1/2 tsp cloves

Instructions:

1. Preheat your oven to 375°F (190°C).

2. In a large mixing bowl, combine the sliced apples and raspberries.

3. Spread the apple and raspberry mixture evenly in the bottom of a greased baking dish.

4. In another bowl, mix together the rolled oats, butter or margarine, brown sugar, cinnamon, and cloves until well combined.

5. Sprinkle the oat mixture evenly over the apple and raspberry mixture in the baking dish.

6. Pour the apple juice over the top of the oats.

7. Bake in the preheated oven for about 40-45 minutes, or until the top is golden brown and the apples are tender.

8. Serve warm, optionally with a scoop of vanilla ice cream or a dollop of whipped cream.

Variation and Tips:

✓ You can use fresh or frozen raspberries for this recipe.

✓ Adjust the amount of sugar according to the sweetness of your apples and personal preference.

✓ Feel free to add other fruits like strawberries or blueberries for added flavor.

✓ Serve leftovers for breakfast with yogurt or as a topping for oatmeal.

✓ Experiment with different spices like nutmeg or ginger for variation.

Nutrition Information (Approximate, per serving):

Calories: 250 Carbohydrates: 48 g Sugars: 26 g Fat: 6 g Protein: 4 g Fiber: 8 g Sodium: 50 mg

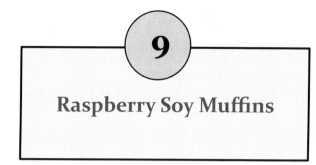

9

Raspberry Soy Muffins

Prep Time: 10 minutes

Cook Time: 20-25 minutes

Servings: 12

Ingredients:

- 1 1/2 cups whole wheat flour
- 1/2 cup soy flour
- 2 tsp baking powder
- 1/3 cup brown sugar
- 2 tsp cinnamon
- 2 egg whites
- 1 cup soy milk
- 2 Tbsp canola oil
- 1 cup raspberries

Instructions:

1. Preheat your oven to 375°F (190°C). Grease or line a muffin tin with paper liners.

2. In a large mixing bowl, combine the whole wheat flour, soy flour, baking powder, brown sugar, and cinnamon.

3. In a separate bowl, whisk together the egg whites, soy milk, and canola oil until well combined.

4. Pour the wet ingredients into the dry ingredients and stir until just combined. Be careful not to overmix.

5. Gently fold in the raspberries.

6. Spoon the batter into the prepared muffin tin, filling each cup about 2/3 full.

7. Bake in the preheated oven for 20-25 minutes, or until a toothpick inserted into the center of a muffin comes out clean.

8. Allow the muffins to cool in the tin for a few minutes before transferring them to a wire rack to cool completely.

Variation and Tips:

✓ You can substitute other berries like blueberries or blackberries for the raspberries.

✓ Feel free to add nuts or seeds for extra texture and flavor.

✓ These muffins freeze well, so you can make a batch ahead of time and store them in an airtight container in the freezer for later use.

✓ Serve them warm with a spread of butter or jam for a delicious breakfast or snack.

Nutrition Information (Approximate, per serving):

Calories: 160 Carbohydrates: 25 g Sugars: 7 g Fat: 5 g Protein: 6 g Fiber: 4 g Sodium: 120 mg

10

Chocolate Black Bean Brownies

Prep Time: 10 minutes

Cook Time: 25-30 minutes

Servings: 12

Ingredients:

- 1 1/2 cups cooked black beans
- 4 large eggs
- 1 tbsp mint extract
- 1 teaspoon stevia
- 5 tbsp vegetable oil
- 1/3 cup honey
- 6 tbsp dark, unsweetened cocoa powder
- 1 tsp baking powder
- 1/2 tsp baking soda
- Pinch of salt
- Fresh mint leaves, for garnish

Instructions:

- Preheat your oven to 350°F (175°C). Grease or line a baking dish with parchment paper.

- Rinse and drain the cooked black beans.

- In a blender or food processor, combine the black beans, eggs, mint extract, stevia, vegetable oil, and honey. Blend until smooth.

- Add the cocoa powder, baking powder, baking soda, and salt to the blender. Blend again until well combined.

- Pour the batter into the prepared baking dish, spreading it out evenly.

- Bake in the preheated oven for 25-30 minutes, or until a toothpick inserted into the center comes out clean.

- Remove from the oven and let the brownies cool in the pan for about 10 minutes.

- Once cooled, cut into squares and garnish with fresh mint leaves if desired.

Variation and Tips:

✓ You can substitute the mint extract with vanilla extract for a different flavor profile.

✓ For a richer chocolate taste, use dark cocoa powder instead of regular cocoa powder.

✓ Add chopped nuts or chocolate chips to the batter for added texture.

✓ Store leftover brownies in an airtight container at room temperature for up to 3 days, or in the refrigerator for longer shelf life.

Nutrition Information (Approximate, per serving):

Calories: 150 Carbohydrates: 18 g Sugars: 10 g Fat: 7 g Protein: 4 g Fiber: 3 g Sodium: 130 mg

SNACKS

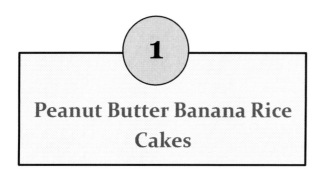

1

Peanut Butter Banana Rice Cakes

Prep Time: 5 minutes

Servings: 1

Ingredients:

- 2 rice cakes
- 2 tablespoons of natural nut butter (almond, peanut, or cashew)
- 1 small ripe banana, sliced

Instructions:

1. Spread 1 tablespoon of nut butter on each rice cake.
2. Arrange the sliced banana on top of the nut butter layer.
3. Press the banana slices slightly into the nut butter for better adherence.
4. Serve immediately and enjoy your quick and delicious peanut butter banana rice cakes!

Variation and Tips:

✓ Add a drizzle of honey or a sprinkle of cinnamon for extra flavor.

✓ Consider using flavored rice cakes, such as cinnamon or chocolate, for added variety.

✓ Top with chia seeds or crushed nuts for additional texture and nutritional benefits.

✓ For a savory twist, try using almond butter with sliced strawberries or cashew butter with blueberries.

Nutrition Information (Approximate, per serving):

Calories: 300 Carbohydrates: 35 g
Protein: 8 g Fat: 16 g Fiber: 5 g Sugar: 12g
Sodium: 75 mg

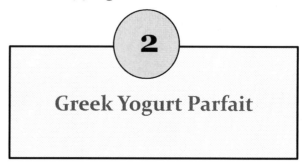

2

Greek Yogurt Parfait

Prep Time: 5 minutes

Servings: 1

Ingredients:

- 1 cup of plain Greek yogurt
- 1/4 cup of granola
- 1/2 cup of mixed berries (strawberries, blueberries, or raspberries)
- 1 tablespoon of honey (optional)

Instructions:

1. In a serving glass or bowl, layer half of the Greek yogurt.
2. Sprinkle half of the granola over the yogurt layer.
3. Add half of the mixed berries on top of the granola.
4. Repeat the layers with the remaining yogurt, granola, and mixed berries.
5. Drizzle honey on top if desired.

6. Serve immediately and enjoy your delicious Greek yogurt parfait!

Variation and Tips:

✓ Experiment with different types of granola, such as nutty or fruity varieties, to suit your taste preferences.

✓ Substitute maple syrup or agave nectar for honey if preferred.

✓ Add a sprinkle of cinnamon or a dash of vanilla extract for extra flavor.

✓ Include sliced bananas or diced mangoes for additional fruit options.

Nutrition Information (Approximate, per serving):

Calories: 300 Carbohydrates: 45 g Protein: 20 g Fat: 7 g Fiber: 5 g Sugar: 25g Sodium: 70 mg

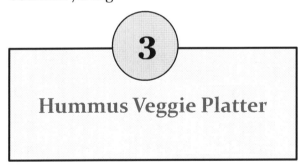

3

Hummus Veggie Platter

Prep Time: 10 minutes

Servings: 2-4

Ingredients:

- 1/2 cup of hummus
- 1 medium carrot, cut into sticks
- 1 medium cucumber, cut into sticks
- 1 bell pepper, sliced

Instructions:

1. Arrange the hummus in a small serving bowl or plate in the center of a larger platter.

2. Surround the hummus with the carrot sticks, cucumber sticks, and sliced bell pepper.

3. Serve immediately and enjoy your delicious and nutritious hummus veggie platter!

Variation and Tips:

✓ Add other vegetables such as cherry tomatoes, celery sticks, or radishes for more variety.

✓ Consider adding some pita bread or whole grain crackers for dipping.

✓ Sprinkle some sesame seeds or chopped fresh herbs on top of the hummus for extra flavor and presentation.

✓ If you prefer, you can make your own hummus at home using chickpeas, tahini, lemon juice, garlic, and olive oil.

Nutrition Information (Approximate, per serving):

Calories: 100 Carbohydrates: 15 g Protein: 5 g Fat: 3 g Fiber: 6 g Sugar: 6 g Sodium: 200 mg

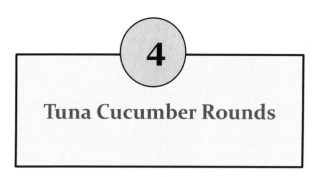

4

Tuna Cucumber Rounds

Prep Time: 10 minutes

Servings: 2-4

Ingredients:

- 1 can of tuna, drained
- 2 tablespoons of Greek yogurt
- 1 tablespoon of lemon juice
- 1/4 cup of diced celery
- Salt and pepper to taste
- 2 large cucumbers, sliced into rounds

Instructions:

1. In a mixing bowl, combine the drained tuna, Greek yogurt, lemon juice, diced celery, salt, and pepper. Mix well until all ingredients are evenly incorporated.
2. Taste and adjust seasoning if needed.
3. Place cucumber rounds on a serving platter or plate.
4. Spoon the tuna mixture onto each cucumber round.
5. Serve immediately and enjoy your tasty and refreshing tuna cucumber rounds!

Variation and Tips:

1. For added flavor, consider adding chopped fresh herbs such as parsley or dill to the tuna mixture.
2. If you prefer a spicier flavor, you can add a pinch of cayenne pepper or a dash of hot sauce to the tuna mixture.
3. Customize the recipe by adding additional vegetables such as diced bell peppers or red onions.
4. You can also serve the tuna mixture on whole grain crackers or toasted bread slices instead of cucumber rounds.

Nutrition Information (Approximate, per serving):

Calories: 100 Carbohydrates: 7 g Protein: 15 g Fat: 2 g Fiber: 2 g Sugar: 3 g Sodium: 200 mg

5

Cinnamon Apple Slices

Prep Time: 5 minutes

Cook Time: 5 minutes

Servings: 2-4

Ingredients:

- 2 large apples, cored and thinly sliced
- 1 teaspoon of ground cinnamon

Instructions:

1. In a large bowl, toss the thinly sliced apples with ground cinnamon until the apples are evenly coated.

2. Heat a non-stick skillet over medium heat.

3. Once the skillet is hot, add the cinnamon-coated apple slices.

4. Cook the apples for about 3-5 minutes, stirring occasionally, until they are tender and lightly caramelized.

5. Remove the skillet from the heat and transfer the cooked apple slices to a serving plate.

6. Serve the cinnamon apple slices warm as a delicious and comforting dessert or snack.

Variation and Tips:

✓ For added sweetness, you can sprinkle a little bit of brown sugar or drizzle honey over the apple slices before cooking.

✓ Serve the cinnamon apple slices with a dollop of Greek yogurt or a scoop of vanilla ice cream for a delightful treat.

✓ Experiment with different apple varieties such as Gala, Honeycrisp, or Granny Smith for varied flavor and texture.

✓ You can also add a splash of lemon juice to the apples to prevent them from browning and to add a hint of tartness to the dish.

Nutrition Information (Approximate, per serving):

Calories: 50 Carbohydrates: 14 g Fiber: 3 g Sugar: 10 g Fat: 0 g Protein: 0 g Sodium: 0 mg

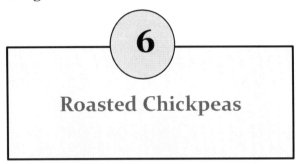

6

Roasted Chickpeas

Prep Time: 5 minutes

Cook Time: 25 minutes

Servings: 2-4

Ingredients:

- 1 can of chickpeas, drained and rinsed
- 1 tablespoon of olive oil
- 1/2 teaspoon of ground cumin
- 1/2 teaspoon of smoked paprika
- Salt and pepper to taste

Instructions:

- Preheat your oven to 400°F (200°C).
- Rinse and drain the chickpeas, then pat them dry with a clean kitchen towel or paper towels to remove excess moisture.
- In a bowl, toss the dried chickpeas with olive oil, ground cumin, smoked paprika, salt, and pepper until evenly coated.

- Spread the seasoned chickpeas in a single layer on a baking sheet lined with parchment paper or aluminum foil.

- Roast the chickpeas in the preheated oven for about 20-25 minutes, shaking the pan halfway through, until they are golden brown and crispy.

- Once done, remove the baking sheet from the oven and let the roasted chickpeas cool slightly before serving.

- Enjoy the roasted chickpeas as a crunchy and flavorful snack or as a topping for salads and soups.

Variation and Tips:

✓ Experiment with different seasonings such as garlic powder, onion powder, chili powder, or curry powder to customize the flavor of the roasted chickpeas.

✓ For extra crispiness, you can increase the baking time slightly or turn on the broiler for the last couple of minutes, but keep a close eye on them to prevent burning.

✓ Store any leftover roasted chickpeas in an airtight container at room temperature for up to 3 days.

✓ Feel free to add the roasted chickpeas to grain bowls, wraps, or Buddha bowls for added protein and crunch.

Nutrition Information (Approximate, per serving):

Calories: 120 Carbohydrates: 16 g Fiber: 5g Sugar: 3 g Fat: 5 g Protein: 5 g Sodium: 190 mg

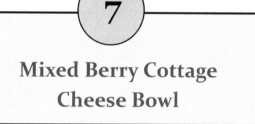

Mixed Berry Cottage Cheese Bowl

Prep Time: 5 minutes

Servings: 1

Ingredients:

- 1/2 cup of low-fat cottage cheese
- 1/2 cup of mixed berries (strawberries, blueberries, or raspberries)
- 1/4 cup of sliced almonds

Instructions:

1. In a serving bowl, place the low-fat cottage cheese.

2. Arrange the mixed berries on top of the cottage cheese.

3. Sprinkle sliced almonds over the berries.

4. Serve immediately as a nutritious and satisfying breakfast or snack.

Variation and Tips:

✓ You can customize this recipe by using your favorite combination of berries or adding other fruits like sliced bananas or peaches.

- Feel free to substitute the sliced almonds with other nuts or seeds such as walnuts, pecans, or pumpkin seeds for added crunch and nutrition.
- To enhance the flavor, you can drizzle a little honey or maple syrup over the cottage cheese and berries.
- Experiment with different textures and flavors by adding granola, chia seeds, or shredded coconut to the bowl.
- This recipe is versatile and can be enjoyed any time of the day as a healthy and delicious option.

Nutrition Information (Approximate, per serving):

Calories: 250 Carbohydrates: 16 g Fiber: 6g Sugar: 8 g Fat: 14 g Protein: 21 g Sodium: 380 mg

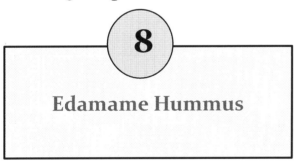

8

Edamame Hummus

Prep Time: 10 minutes

Servings: 4

Ingredients:

- 1 cup of shelled edamame
- 1/4 cup of tahini
- 1/4 cup of lemon juice
- 2 cloves of garlic, minced
- 1/2 teaspoon of ground cumin
- Salt and pepper to taste

Instructions:

1. In a pot of boiling water, cook the shelled edamame for about 3-5 minutes or until tender. Drain and set aside to cool slightly.
2. In a food processor, combine the cooked edamame, tahini, lemon juice, minced garlic, and ground cumin.
3. Blend until smooth, scraping down the sides of the food processor as needed to ensure even mixing.
4. Season with salt and pepper to taste, and blend again until well combined.
5. Transfer the edamame hummus to a serving bowl.
6. Serve with your favorite vegetables, crackers, or pita bread for dipping.

Variation and Tips:

- For added flavor, you can incorporate fresh herbs like parsley, cilantro, or basil into the hummus.
- Adjust the consistency of the hummus by adding more lemon juice or a splash of water if desired.
- Customize the seasoning by adding spices like paprika, chili powder, or cayenne pepper for a kick of heat.
- Store any leftover hummus in an airtight container in the refrigerator for up to 5 days.

Nutrition Information (Approximate, per serving):

Calories: 120 Carbohydrates: 9 g Fiber: 3g Sugar: 1 g Fat: 8 g Protein: 6 g Sodium: 10 mg

9

Avocado Toast

Prep Time: 5 minutes

Servings: 1

Ingredients:

- 2 slices of whole-grain bread
- 1 ripe avocado, mashed
- 1/2 teaspoon of lemon juice
- Salt and pepper to taste

Instructions:

1. Toast the slices of whole-grain bread until golden brown.
2. In a small bowl, mash the ripe avocado with a fork until smooth.
3. Stir in the lemon juice, salt, and pepper, combining well.
4. Spread the mashed avocado mixture evenly onto the toasted bread slices.
5. Serve immediately and enjoy!

Variation and Tips:

- ✓ Customize your avocado toast by adding toppings like sliced tomatoes, radishes, poached eggs, or crumbled feta cheese.
- ✓ For extra flavor, sprinkle some red pepper flakes, sesame seeds, or everything bagel seasoning on top.
- ✓ Drizzle a bit of balsamic glaze or hot sauce over the avocado toast for added tanginess or spiciness.
- ✓ Experiment with different types of bread, such as sourdough, rye, or multigrain, for varied texture and flavor.

Nutrition Information (Approximate, per serving):

Calories: 250 Carbohydrates: 28 g Fiber: 9 g Sugar: 2 g Fat: 14 g Protein: 7 g Sodium: 230 mg

10

Mixed Nut and Seed Trail Mix

Prep Time: 5 minutes

Servings: 6

Ingredients:

- 1/2 cup unsalted almonds
- 1/2 cup unsalted cashews
- 1/2 cup unsalted pumpkin seeds
- 1/2 cup unsweetened dried cranberries

- 1/2 cup unsweetened dried apricots, chopped

Instructions:

1. In a large bowl, combine the unsalted almonds, cashews, pumpkin seeds, dried cranberries, and chopped dried apricots.

2. Toss the ingredients together until evenly mixed.

3. Portion the trail mix into individual serving sizes or store it in an airtight container for later use.

Variation and Tips:

✓ Feel free to customize the trail mix by adding other nuts, seeds, or dried fruits such as walnuts, pecans, sunflower seeds, raisins, or dried cherries.

✓ For extra flavor, you can lightly toast the nuts and seeds in a dry skillet over medium heat before mixing them with the dried fruits.

✓ Adjust the quantities of each ingredient according to your preference, keeping in mind the desired balance of flavors and textures.

✓ This trail mix is perfect for snacking on the go, hiking, or as a topping for yogurt, oatmeal, or salads.

Nutrition Information (Approximate, per serving):

Calories: 250 Carbohydrates: 20 g Fiber: 4 g Sugar: 10 g Fat: 15 g Protein: 7 g Sodium: 5 mg

BEVERAGES

1

Lime and Mint Infused Water

Prep Time: 5 minutes

Cook Time: 0 minutes

Servings: 4

Ingredients:

- 1 lime, sliced
- 1 handful fresh mint leaves
- 4 cups water

Instructions:

1. In a large pitcher, combine the lime slices and fresh mint leaves.

2. Fill the pitcher with 4 cups of water.

3. Stir gently to mix the ingredients.

4. Refrigerate the infused water for at least 1 hour to allow the flavors to meld.

5. Serve the lime and mint infused water over ice, if desired, and garnish with additional lime slices and mint leaves for presentation.

Variation and Tips:

- ✓ For added sweetness, you can include a few slices of fresh cucumber or a teaspoon of honey.

- ✓ Experiment with other citrus fruits such as lemon or orange to create different flavor profiles.

- ✓ Adjust the amount of mint leaves according to your preference for mint flavor intensity.

- ✓ This refreshing infused water is perfect for staying hydrated throughout the day and can be enjoyed as a healthy alternative to sugary beverages.

Nutrition Information (Approximate, per serving):

Calories: 0 kcal Carbohydrates: 0 g Fiber: 0 g Sugar: 0 g Fat: 0 g Protein: 0 g Sodium: 0 mg

2

Berry Banana Chia Seed Smoothie

Prep Time: 5 minutes

Cook Time: 0 minutes

Servings: 1

Ingredients:

- 1 cup mixed frozen berries
- 1/2 banana
- 1/2 cup unsweetened almond milk
- 1/2 cup water
- 1 tbsp chia seeds

Instructions:

1. In a blender, combine the mixed frozen berries, banana, unsweetened almond milk, water, and chia seeds.

2. Blend on high speed until smooth and well combined, ensuring that the chia seeds are fully incorporated.

3. If the smoothie is too thick, add more water as needed until desired consistency is reached.

4. Pour the smoothie into a glass and serve immediately.

5. Enjoy this nutritious and delicious berry banana chia seed smoothie as a refreshing breakfast or snack option!

Variation and Tips:

✓ Feel free to customize this smoothie by adding other fruits such as strawberries, blueberries, or mango.

✓ Substitute any milk of your choice for the unsweetened almond milk, such as soy milk or coconut milk.

✓ For added sweetness, you can include a drizzle of honey or maple syrup.

✓ Experiment with different toppings such as granola, shredded coconut, or additional fresh fruit slices.

Nutrition Information (Approximate, per serving):

Calories: 180 Carbohydrates: 31 g Fiber: 10 gSugar: 13 g Fat: 6 g Protein: 4 g Sodium: 85 mg

3

Golden Turmeric Latte

Prep Time: 5 minutes

Cook Time: 5 minutes

Servings: 1

Ingredients:

- 1 cup unsweetened almond milk
- 1 tsp ground turmeric
- 1/2 tsp ground cinnamon
- 1/4 tsp ground ginger
- 1/4 tsp ground cardamom
- 1 tsp honey

Instructions:

1. In a small saucepan, heat the unsweetened almond milk over medium heat until it begins to simmer.

2. Add the ground turmeric, ground cinnamon, ground ginger, and ground cardamom to the saucepan.

3. Whisk the mixture continuously until the spices are well combined and the milk is heated through, about 3-5 minutes.

4. Remove the saucepan from the heat and stir in the honey until it is fully dissolved.

5. Pour the golden turmeric latte into a mug and serve hot.

6. Enjoy this cozy and comforting beverage as a soothing treat any time of the day!

Variation and Tips:

✓ Feel free to adjust the spices and sweetness level to suit your taste preferences. You can add more or less honey, or adjust the amounts of turmeric, cinnamon, ginger, and cardamom.

✓ For a creamier texture, you can substitute coconut milk or regular milk for the unsweetened almond milk.

✓ Garnish the latte with a sprinkle of ground cinnamon or a cinnamon stick for added flavor and presentation.

✓ This latte can be enjoyed warm or chilled over ice for a refreshing twist.

Nutrition Information (Approximate, per serving):

Calories: 70 Carbohydrates: 13 gFiber: 1 g Sugar: 10 g Fat: 2 g Protein: 1 g Sodium: 160 mg

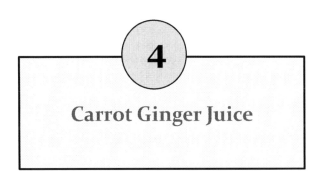

4

Carrot Ginger Juice

Prep Time: 10 minutes

Cook Time: 0 minutes

Servings: 1

Ingredients:

- 4 medium carrots
- 1 inch piece of ginger
- 1/2 lemon, juiced

Instructions:

1. Wash and peel the carrots. Cut them into smaller pieces if needed to fit into your juicer chute.

2. Peel the ginger and cut it into smaller pieces.

3. Juice the carrots and ginger together according to your juicer's instructions.

4. Once juiced, stir in the freshly squeezed lemon juice.

5. Pour the juice into a glass and serve immediately over ice if desired.

Variation and Tips:

✓ Feel free to adjust the amount of ginger and lemon juice to suit your taste preferences.

✓ If you prefer a sweeter juice, you can add a small apple or a splash of orange juice to the mixture.

- ✓ For an extra kick, you can add a pinch of ground turmeric or a few sprigs of fresh mint.
- ✓ This juice is best enjoyed fresh, but you can store any leftovers in an airtight container in the refrigerator for up to 24 hours.

Nutrition Information (Approximate, per serving):

Calories: 80 kcal Carbohydrates: 19 g Fiber: 5 g Sugar: 9 g Fat: 0 g Protein: 2 g Sodium: 90 mg

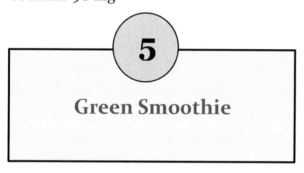

5

Green Smoothie

Prep Time: 5 minutes

Cook Time: 0 minutes

Servings: 1

Ingredients:

- 1 cup spinach
- 1/2 cup frozen pineapple
- 1/2 cup frozen mango
- 1/2 banana
- 1/2 cup unsweetened almond milk
- 1/2 cup water

Instructions:

1. Place all the ingredients in a blender.

2. Blend until smooth and creamy, adding more water if necessary to reach your desired consistency.

3. Pour the smoothie into a glass and serve immediately.

Variation and Tips:

- ✓ You can add a scoop of protein powder or Greek yogurt for an extra protein boost.
- ✓ Feel free to substitute any of the frozen fruits with your favorites, such as berries or peaches.
- ✓ For a thicker smoothie, you can use more frozen fruits or less liquid.
- ✓ To make it sweeter, you can add a drizzle of honey or maple syrup.
- ✓ Customize your smoothie with additional ingredients like chia seeds, flaxseeds, or a handful of nuts for added nutrition.

Nutrition Information (Approximate, per serving):

Calories: 250 Carbohydrates: 58 g Fiber: 9 g Sugar: 35 g Fat: 3 g Protein: 4 g Sodium: 120 mg

6

Turmeric Golden Milk

Prep Time: 5 minutes

Cook Time: 5 minutes

Servings: 1

Ingredients:

- 1 cup unsweetened almond milk
- 1 tsp ground turmeric (Curcuma longa)
- 1 tsp coconut oil
- 1 tsp maple syrup (optional)
- 1/8 tsp black pepper
- 1/8 tsp ground cinnamon
- 1/8 tsp ground ginger

Instructions:

1. In a small saucepan, heat the almond milk over medium heat until it begins to simmer.

2. Add the ground turmeric, coconut oil, maple syrup (if using), black pepper, cinnamon, and ginger to the saucepan.

3. Whisk the ingredients together until well combined.

4. Reduce the heat to low and let the mixture simmer for about 5 minutes, stirring occasionally.

5. Once heated through, pour the golden milk into a mug and serve warm.

Variation and Tips:

✓ You can adjust the sweetness by adding more or less maple syrup according to your taste preference.

✓ Feel free to customize the spices to your liking. You can increase or decrease the amounts of cinnamon, ginger, and black pepper based on your taste.

✓ For a creamier texture, you can use coconut milk instead of almond milk.

✓ Turmeric stains easily, so be careful when handling it and avoid contact with clothing or surfaces that can be stained.

Nutrition Information (Approximate, per serving):

Calories: 100 Carbohydrates: 9 g Fat: 7 g Protein: 1 g Sodium: 160 mg

7

Mixed Berry Protein Smoothie

Prep Time: 5 minutes

Cook Time: 0 minutes

Servings: 1

Ingredients:

- 1 cup plain Greek yogurt
- 1 cup frozen mixed berries (such as strawberries, blueberries, raspberries)

- 1/2 cup milk or milk alternative (almond milk, soy milk, etc.)
- 1 scoop protein powder (whey, soy, egg, or pea protein)
- 1 tablespoon ground flaxseeds or chia seeds
- 1/4 avocado or 1 tablespoon nut butter (optional)

Instructions:

1. In a blender, combine the plain Greek yogurt, frozen mixed berries, milk or milk alternative, protein powder, and ground flaxseeds or chia seeds.
2. If desired, add the optional avocado or nut butter for added creaminess and healthy fats.
3. Blend until smooth and creamy, scraping down the sides of the blender as needed to ensure all ingredients are well incorporated.
4. Once smooth, pour the smoothie into a glass and serve immediately.

Variation and Tips:

✓ Feel free to customize the smoothie with your choice of frozen fruit. Mango or pineapple can also be used instead of mixed berries.

✓ Adjust the consistency by adding more or less milk, depending on your preference for thickness.

✓ If you prefer a sweeter smoothie, you can add a natural sweetener such as honey, maple syrup, or stevia.

✓ To make it a green smoothie, add a handful of spinach or kale for added nutrients.

✓ Experiment with different flavors of protein powder to find your favorite combination.

✓ This smoothie is a great post-workout snack or breakfast option for a quick and nutritious meal on the go.

Nutrition Information (Approximate, per serving):

Calories: 350 Carbohydrates: 35 g Protein: 30 g Fat: 12 g Fiber: 10 g Sugar: 20 g

8

Blueberry Compote

Prep Time: 5 minutes

Cook Time: 10 minutes

Servings: Makes about 2 cups

Ingredients:

- 4 cups blueberries
- 2 cups water
- 1/2 cup sugar
- 4 tablespoons potato starch

Instructions:

1. In a medium saucepan, combine the blueberries and water. Bring to a boil over medium-high heat.

2. Reduce the heat to low and simmer for about 5 minutes, or until the blueberries start to break down and release their juices.

3. In a small bowl, mix the sugar and potato starch until well combined.

4. Gradually stir the sugar and starch mixture into the simmering blueberries, stirring constantly to prevent lumps from forming.

5. Continue to cook for another 3-5 minutes, or until the mixture has thickened to your desired consistency.

6. Remove the compote from the heat and let it cool slightly before serving.

7. Serve the blueberry compote warm or chilled over pancakes, waffles, yogurt, ice cream, or any other dessert of your choice.

Variations and Tips:

✓ You can adjust the sweetness of the compote by adding more or less sugar according to your taste preference.

✓ Feel free to substitute other berries or fruits for the blueberries, such as strawberries, raspberries, blackberries, or peaches.

✓ If you prefer a smoother compote, you can puree the mixture with an immersion blender before serving.

✓ Store any leftover compote in an airtight container in the refrigerator for up to one week. It can also be frozen for longer storage.

Nutrition Information (Approximate, per serving):

Calories: 70 Carbohydrates: 18 g Fiber: 2g Sugars: 12 g Fat: 0 g Protein: 0 g

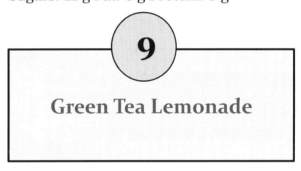

9

Green Tea Lemonade

Prep Time: 5 minutes

Cook Time: 5 minutes

Servings: 2 cups

Ingredients:

- 2 cups water
- 2 1/2 teaspoons loose green tea leaves (loose leaves release more catechins than tea bags)
- 3 tablespoons freshly pressed organic lemon juice

Instructions:

1. In a small saucepan, bring the water to a boil.

2. Remove the saucepan from the heat and add the loose green tea leaves to the hot water.

3. Let the tea steep for about 3-5 minutes, depending on your preference for strength.

4. Strain the tea leaves from the water using a fine-mesh strainer or a tea infuser.

5. Allow the tea to cool to room temperature.

6. Once cooled, stir in the freshly pressed organic lemon juice.

7. Transfer the green tea lemonade to a pitcher or individual glasses filled with ice.

8. Serve immediately and enjoy the refreshing taste of homemade green tea lemonade.

Variations and Tips:

✓ For added sweetness, you can stir in honey, agave nectar, or simple syrup to taste.

✓ Garnish the green tea lemonade with lemon slices or mint leaves for an extra burst of flavor and visual appeal.

✓ Feel free to adjust the amount of lemon juice according to your preference for tartness.

✓ You can also experiment with different types of green tea, such as sencha, matcha, or jasmine green tea, to vary the flavor profile of the lemonade.

✓ Store any leftover green tea lemonade in the refrigerator for up to 2 days. Be sure to stir or shake it well before serving, as the lemon juice may settle at the bottom over time.

Nutrition Information (Approximate, per serving):

Calories: 10 Carbohydrates: 3 g Fiber: 0 g Sugars: 0 g Fat: 0 g Protein: 0 g

10

Mango Green Tea Smoothie

Prep Time: 10 minutes

Cook Time: 5 minutes

Servings: 2

Ingredients:

• 2 cups mango, peeled and chopped

• 1 cup green tea made from loose leaves

• 1 tablespoon honey

• 1/2 inch piece fresh ginger, peeled and finely chopped

• 1 cup crushed ice

Instructions:

1. Brew the green tea using loose leaves and let it cool to room temperature.

2. In a blender, combine the chopped mango, cooled green tea, honey, finely chopped ginger, and crushed ice.

3. Blend until smooth and creamy, adjusting the consistency with more ice or water if desired.

4. Once blended to your liking, pour the smoothie into glasses and serve immediately.

5. Optionally, garnish with a slice of mango or a sprig of fresh mint for an extra touch of freshness.

Variations and Tips:

✓ For added creaminess, you can include a splash of coconut milk or yogurt in the smoothie.

✓ If you prefer a sweeter taste, you can increase the amount of honey or add a ripe banana to the mix.

✓ Experiment with different fruits such as pineapple or papaya for a tropical twist.

✓ Feel free to customize the smoothie by adding your favorite spices or superfood powders, such as turmeric or chia seeds, for extra nutrition.

✓ To make the smoothie ahead of time, prepare the ingredients and store them separately in the refrigerator until ready to blend.

✓ This smoothie is a refreshing and nutritious option for breakfast or as a midday snack, providing a boost of energy and antioxidants.

Nutrition Information (Approximate, per serving):

Calories: 150 Carbohydrates: 38 g Fiber: 3 g Sugars: 33 g Fat: 0.5 g Protein: 1 g

CONCLUSION

As we reach the final pages of the "Pancreatic Cancer Diet Cookbook," I want to extend my heartfelt appreciation for embarking on this journey toward improved health with me. Throughout these recipes, tips, and insights, we've aimed to provide you with nourishing and delicious options to support your battle against pancreatic cancer and enhance your overall well-being.

As you close this book, I offer you a few parting thoughts to carry forward. Remember the importance of being mindful of your dietary choices and the impact they can have on managing pancreatic cancer. Pay attention to nutritional labels, particularly regarding fat, sugar, and fiber content, and strive to make informed decisions that align with your health goals.

In addition to monitoring nutritional content, practicing portion control is essential. By moderating your serving sizes, you can better regulate your nutrient intake and optimize your body's ability to fight against cancer cells.

But beyond the specifics of what you eat, it's crucial to recognize that this journey is about more than just food—it's about embracing a holistic approach to health. Cultivate a lifestyle that nourishes not only your body but also your mind and spirit. Find joy in the abundance of wholesome foods available to you, experiment with flavors and textures, and savor each meal as a testament to your commitment to self-care and healing.

As you continue on your path toward wellness, remember that you are not alone. Draw strength from the knowledge and resources provided in this book, and don't hesitate to seek support from loved ones, healthcare professionals, and support groups specializing in pancreatic cancer.

Finally, I want to express my sincerest gratitude to you, dear reader, for entrusting me with a part of your health journey. Your resilience and determination are truly inspiring, and it has been an honor to support you in your fight against pancreatic cancer.

Please note that the nutrition information provided in this book is an estimate and may vary based on factors such as serving sizes and ingredient substitutions. Therefore, I encourage you to use this information as a guideline and consult with a healthcare professional or registered dietitian for personalized dietary advice.

With heartfelt appreciation and warm regards,

Mary B. Lax

4 WEEKS MEAL PLAN

WEEK 1

Day 1:

Breakfast: Antioxidant Muffins

Lunch: Avocado Carrot Salad

Dinner: Herb-Marinated Chicken Breasts

Snack/Dessert: Mixed Berry Protein Smoothie

Day 2:

Breakfast: Potato and Herb Omelet

Lunch: Broccoli Barley Soup

Dinner: Lemon Dill Salmon

Snack/Dessert: Greek Yogurt Parfait

Day 3:

Breakfast: Ricotta and Strawberry Basil Toast

Lunch: Quinoa and Black Bean Salad

Dinner: Garlic Shrimp Zoodles

Snack/Dessert: Cinnamon Apple Slices

Day 4:

Breakfast: Pumpkin Spice Overnight Oats

Lunch: Chicken Vegetable Soup

Dinner: Butternut Squash and Chickpea Curry

Snack/Dessert: Mango Green Tea Smoothie

Day 5:

Breakfast: Apricot Pecan Breakfast Bars

Lunch: Salmon and Cherry Tomato Salad

Dinner: Tofu Stir-Fry

Snack/Dessert: Nettle Pancakes with Raspberry Sauce

Day 6:

Breakfast: Peanut Butter Banana Chia Toast

Lunch: Curried Sweet Potato Soup

Dinner: Baked White Fish with Vegetables

Snack/Dessert: Hummus Veggie Platter

Day 7:

Breakfast: Cottage Cheese, Cucumber, and Tomato Toast

Lunch: Pear and Radicchio Salad

Dinner: Lentil Shepherd's Pie

Snack/Dessert: Berry Smoothie with Flaxseed

WEEK 2

Day 8:

Breakfast: Purple Grape Jam Pancakes

Lunch: Cucumber and Tomato Salad

Dinner: Coconut Fish Curry with Brown Rice

Snack/Dessert: Apple-Raspberry Crisp

Day 9:

Breakfast: Blueberry Compote

Lunch: Strawberry Fennel Salad

Dinner: Quinoa Stuffed Bell Peppers

Snack/Dessert: Mixed Nut and Seed Trail Mix

Day 10:

Breakfast: Chocolate Black Bean Brownies

Lunch: Beet and Carrot Salad

Dinner: Roasted Chicken Thighs with Root Vegetables

Snack/Dessert: Golden Turmeric Latte

Day 11:

Breakfast: Mango Green Tea Smoothie

Lunch: Arugula and Tomato Salad with Avocado

Dinner: Stir-Fried Shrimp with Mixed Vegetables

Snack/Dessert: Lime and Mint Infused Water

Day 12:

Breakfast: Raspberry Soy Muffins

Lunch: Garlic and Tomato Soup

Dinner: Turkey Meatballs in Tomato Sauce

Snack/Dessert: Greek Yogurt Parfait

Day 13:

Breakfast: Gluten-Free Carrot Muffins

Lunch: Smoked Salmon Salad

Dinner: Nettle Pesto Pasta

Snack/Dessert: Carrot Ginger Juice

Day 14:

Breakfast: Berry Banana Chia Seed Smoothie

Lunch: Apple and Onion Soup

Dinner: Lentil Stir-Fry

Snack/Dessert: Mixed Berry Cottage Cheese Bowl

WEEK 3

Day 15:

Breakfast: Peanut Butter Banana Rice Cakes

Lunch: Beet and Carrot Salad

Dinner: Lentil Stir-Fry

Snack/Dessert: Lime and Mint Infused Water

Day 16:

Breakfast: Apple Raspberry Crisp

Lunch: Broccoli Apple Salad

Dinner: Tofu Stir-Fry with Nettle Pesto Pasta

Snack/Dessert: Mixed Nut and Seed Trail Mix

Day 17:

Breakfast: Cinnamon Apple Slices

Lunch: Avocado Carrot Salad

Dinner: Garlic Shrimp Zoodles

Snack/Dessert: Berry Banana Chia Seed Smoothie

Day 18:

Breakfast: Mango Green Tea Smoothie

Lunch: Strawberry Fennel Salad

Dinner: Quinoa and Black Bean Salad

Snack/Dessert: Golden Turmeric Latte

Day 19:

Breakfast: Peanut Butter Banana Chia Toast

Lunch: Smoked Salmon Salad

Dinner: Lentil Shepherd's Pie

Snack/Dessert: Greek Yogurt Parfait

Day 20:

Breakfast: Apricot Pecan Breakfast Bars

Lunch: Arugula and Tomato Salad with Avocado

Dinner: Lemon Dill Salmon

Snack/Dessert: Apple-Raspberry Crisp

Day 21:

Breakfast: Quinoa Breakfast Bowl

Lunch: Chicken and Vegetable Soup

Dinner: Coconut Fish Curry with Brown Rice

Snack/Dessert: Mixed Berry Protein Smoothie

WEEK 4

Day 22:

Breakfast: Berry Smoothie with Flaxseed

Lunch: Pear and Radicchio Salad

Dinner: Herb-Marinated Chicken Breasts

Snack/Dessert: Chocolate Black Bean Brownies

Day 23:

Breakfast: Ricotta and Strawberry Basil Toast

Lunch: Beet and Carrot Soup

Dinner: Quinoa Stuffed Bell Peppers

Snack/Dessert: Mango Green Tea Smoothie

Day 24:

Breakfast: Pumpkin Spice Overnight Oats

Lunch: Carrot, Fennel, and Cucumber Salad

Dinner: Roasted Chicken Thighs with Root Vegetables

Snack/Dessert: Cinnamon Apple Slices

Day 25:

Breakfast: Blueberry Compote

Lunch: Broccoli Barley Soup

Dinner: Butternut Squash Soup

Snack/Dessert: Raspberry Soy Muffins

Day 26:

Breakfast: Peanut Butter Banana Chia Toast

Lunch: Cucumber and Tomato Salad

Dinner: Mushroom and Shrimp Brown Rice Pilaf

Snack/Dessert: Greek Yogurt Parfait

Day 27:

Breakfast: Cottage Cheese, Cucumber, and Tomato Toast

Lunch: Salmon and Cherry Tomato Salad

Dinner: Lentil Stir-Fry

Snack/Dessert: Lime and Mint Infused Water

Day 28:

Breakfast: Mixed Berry Cottage Cheese Bowl

Lunch: Apple and Onion Soup

Dinner: Turkey Meatballs in Tomato Sauce

Snack/Dessert: Apple Raspberry Crisp

MEAL PREP TIPS

BREAKFAST RECIPES

Antioxidant Muffins:

- Bake a batch of muffins at the beginning of the week and store them in an airtight container for quick breakfasts or snacks throughout the week.

Potato and Herb Omelet:

- Chop and prepare all the ingredients ahead of time, so they're ready to go when you're ready to cook. You can even pre-cook the potatoes slightly to speed up the omelet-making process.

Ricotta and Strawberry Basil Toast:

- Prepare the ricotta spread in advance and keep it refrigerated. Slice the strawberries and chop the basil, then assemble the toasts just before serving for a fresh taste.

Pumpkin Spice Overnight Oats:

- Mix the oats, pumpkin spice, and liquid the night before and let them sit in the refrigerator overnight. In the morning, top with desired fruits and nuts for a quick and nutritious breakfast.

Apricot Pecan Breakfast Bars:

- Make a batch of breakfast bars on the weekend and store them in an airtight container for a grab-and-go breakfast option throughout the week.

Peanut Butter Banana Chia Toast:

- Toast the bread and spread with peanut butter in advance. Slice the bananas and assemble the toasts just before serving for a quick and satisfying breakfast or snack.

Cottage Cheese, Cucumber, and Tomato Toast:

- Toast the bread and prepare the toppings in advance. Assemble the toasts just before serving for a fresh and delicious breakfast option.

Quinoa Breakfast Bowl

- Cook a larger batch of quinoa in advance and store it in the refrigerator for up to 3-4 days. When ready to prepare your breakfast bowls, simply reheat the desired amount of quinoa in the microwave or on the stovetop and proceed with warming the almond milk and assembling the toppings.

Purple Grape Jam Pancakes:

- Make a batch of pancake batter and cook the pancakes in advance. Reheat them in the toaster or microwave for a quick breakfast option.

Breakfast Quesadillas:

- Prepare the quesadilla fillings in advance and assemble them just before cooking. You can also cook the quesadillas ahead of time and reheat them in the microwave or oven for a quick breakfast or snack.

SALADS

Avocado Carrot Salad:

- Peel and chop the carrots in advance, and store them in an airtight container in the refrigerator. Slice the avocado just before serving to prevent browning.

Broccoli Apple Salad:

- Wash and chop the broccoli and apple ahead of time. Toss them with lemon juice to prevent browning. Store the salad ingredients separately and assemble just before serving.

Strawberry Fennel Salad:

- Wash and slice the strawberries and fennel in advance. Store them separately from the salad greens to keep them fresh. Assemble the salad just before serving and dress with vinaigrette.

Arugula and Tomato Salad with Avocado:

- Wash and dry the arugula and tomatoes ahead of time. Slice the avocado just before serving to prevent browning. Toss the salad ingredients together with vinaigrette just before serving.

Pear and Radicchio Salad:

- Wash and slice the pears and radicchio in advance. Toss them with lemon juice to prevent browning. Assemble the salad just before serving and dress with vinaigrette.

Smoked Salmon Salad:

- Flake the smoked salmon into bite-sized pieces and store it in an airtight container in the refrigerator. Wash and dry the salad greens and slice the cucumber. Assemble the salad just before serving and top with smoked salmon.

Carrot, Fennel, and Cucumber Salad:

- Wash and slice the carrots, fennel, and cucumber in advance. Store them separately and assemble the salad just before serving. Dress with vinaigrette and toss well.

Cucumber and Tomato Salad:

- Wash and chop the cucumbers and tomatoes in advance. Store them separately and assemble the salad just before serving. Dress with vinaigrette and toss well.

Beet and Carrot Salad:

- Wash, peel, and grate the beets and carrots in advance. Store them separately and assemble the salad just before serving. Dress with vinaigrette and toss well.

Salmon and Cherry Tomato Salad:

- Cook and flake the salmon ahead of time. Wash and halve the cherry tomatoes. Assemble the salad just before serving and toss with vinaigrette.

MAIN DISH

Herb-Marinated Chicken Breasts:

- Marinate the chicken breasts in advance with your choice of herbs, olive oil, garlic, and lemon juice. Store them in an airtight container in the refrigerator until ready to cook.

Lemon Dill Salmon:

- Prepare the lemon dill marinade in advance and marinate the salmon fillets for a few hours or overnight in the refrigerator. This allows the flavors to develop. Cook the salmon just before serving.

Lentil Stir-Fry:

- Cook the lentils ahead of time and store them in the refrigerator. Chop and prepare the vegetables for the stir-fry in advance. Stir-fry everything together just before serving.

Quinoa and Black Bean Salad:

- Cook the quinoa and black beans in advance and store them separately in the refrigerator. Chop and prepare the vegetables and herbs for the salad. Assemble everything just before serving and toss with dressing.

Tofu Stir-Fry:

- Press and cube the tofu in advance. Chop and prepare the vegetables for the stir-fry. Stir-fry everything together just before serving.

Garlic Shrimp Zoodles:

- Peel and devein the shrimp ahead of time. Spiralize the zucchini into noodles and store them in the refrigerator. Cook the shrimp and zoodles just before serving.

Chicken Vegetable Soup:

- Prepare all the vegetables for the soup in advance and store them in the refrigerator. Cook the chicken and vegetables together with broth just before serving.

Lentil Shepherd's Pie:

- Cook the lentils and prepare the mashed potatoes in advance. Assemble the shepherd's pie and bake just before serving.

Butternut Squash and Chickpea Curry:

- Peel, chop, and roast the butternut squash in advance. Cook the chickpea curry just before serving and serve over roasted squash.

Nettle Pesto Pasta:

- Prepare the nettle pesto in advance and store it in the refrigerator. Cook the pasta just before serving and toss with the pesto.

Mushroom and Shrimp Brown Rice Pilaf:

- Cook the brown rice in advance and store it in the refrigerator. Prepare the mushrooms and shrimp for the pilaf.

Stir-fry everything together just before you serve.

Coconut Fish Curry with Brown Rice:

- Marinate the fish in advance with coconut milk, curry paste, and spices. Cook the brown rice separately. Just before serving, cook the marinated fish in the curry sauce and serve over cooked brown rice.

Turkey Meatballs in Tomato Sauce:

- Prepare the turkey meatballs in advance and store them in the refrigerator. Cook the tomato sauce separately. Just before serving, simmer the meatballs in the tomato sauce until cooked through.

Roasted Chicken Thighs with Root Vegetables:

- Marinate the chicken thighs in advance with herbs, olive oil, and garlic. Peel and chop the root vegetables. Just before serving, roast the marinated chicken thighs and vegetables together in the oven until cooked through.

Quinoa Stuffed Bell Peppers:

- Cook the quinoa in advance and prepare the stuffing mixture with vegetables, beans, and spices. Cut the bell peppers in half and remove the seeds. Stuff the peppers with the quinoa mixture and bake until tender.

Turkey and Vegetable Skewers:

- Marinate the turkey and vegetables in advance with olive oil, lemon juice, and herbs. Skewer the turkey and vegetables onto wooden or metal skewers. Just before serving, grill or bake the skewers until cooked through.

Curried Lentil and Rice Pilaf:

- Cook the lentils and rice separately in advance. Prepare the curry sauce with vegetables and spices. Just before serving, combine the cooked lentils, rice, and curry sauce together and heat through.

Roasted Chicken Thighs with Root Vegetables:

- Marinate the chicken thighs in advance with herbs, olive oil, and garlic. Peel and chop the root vegetables. Just before serving, roast the marinated chicken thighs and vegetables together in the oven until cooked through.

Baked White Fish with Vegetables:

- Marinate the fish in advance with lemon juice, herbs, and olive oil. Prepare the vegetables by chopping and seasoning them. Just before serving, bake the marinated fish and vegetables together until cooked through.

Stir-Fried Shrimp with Mixed Vegetables:

- Peel and devein the shrimp in advance. Chop and prepare the mixed vegetables. Just before serving, stir-fry the shrimp and vegetables together in a hot skillet until cooked through

SOUPS

Broccoli Barley Soup:

- Cook barley separately according to package instructions. Prepare the soup base with broccoli, onions, garlic, and vegetable broth. Combine cooked barley with the soup base just before serving.

Curried Sweet Potato Soup:

- Roast sweet potatoes in advance until tender. Sauté onions, garlic, and curry powder. Blend roasted sweet potatoes with sautéed ingredients and vegetable broth. Reheat and garnish with coconut milk before serving.

Creamy Nettle and Spinach Soup:

- Cook nettles and spinach separately until wilted. Sauté onions and garlic. Blend cooked nettles, spinach, onions, garlic, and vegetable broth until smooth. Reheat and stir in cream or coconut milk before serving.

Pea and Watercress Soup:

- Cook peas and watercress separately until tender. Sauté onions and garlic. Blend cooked peas, watercress, onions, garlic, and vegetable broth until smooth. Reheat before serving.

Garlic and Tomato Soup:

- Sauté garlic and onions until fragrant. Add tomatoes and cook until softened. Blend mixture until smooth. Reheat before serving.

Beet and Carrot Soup:

- Roast beets and carrots until tender. Sauté onions and garlic. Blend roasted vegetables with sautéed ingredients and vegetable broth. Reheat before serving.

Apple and Onion Soup:

- Sauté apples and onions until softened. Add vegetable broth and simmer until flavors combine. Blend mixture until smooth. Reheat before serving.

Chicken and Vegetable Soup:

- Cook chicken and chop into bite-sized pieces. Sauté onions, garlic, and vegetables. Add chicken, vegetables, and broth to a pot and simmer until heated through.

Miso Soup with Tofu and Wakame:

- Prepare miso paste according to package instructions. Add tofu, wakame, and vegetables to broth and simmer until heated through. Stir in miso paste just before serving.

Butternut Squash Soup:

- Roast butternut squash until tender. Sauté onions and garlic. Blend roasted squash with sautéed ingredients and vegetable broth. Reheat and garnish with cream or coconut milk before serving.

DESSERTS

Cinnamon Apple Slices:

- Prepare a large batch of cinnamon sugar mix and store it in an airtight container. Slice apples and toss them in lemon juice to prevent browning. Sprinkle with the cinnamon sugar mix just before serving.

Mango Green Tea Smoothie:

- Pre-portion ripe mango chunks and spinach leaves into freezer bags. Add a tea bag of green tea to each bag. When ready to prepare, simply blend the frozen ingredients with your choice of liquid until smooth.

Berry Smoothie with Flaxseed:

- Wash and freeze mixed berries on a baking sheet before transferring them to freezer bags. Store ground flaxseed in a separate container. When ready to make the smoothie, combine the frozen berries, flaxseed, and liquid in a blender.

Gluten-Free Carrot Muffins:

- Bake a batch of gluten-free carrot muffins and allow them to cool completely. Once cooled, individually wrap the muffins in plastic wrap or store them in airtight containers. They can be refrigerated for up to a week or frozen for longer storage.

Blueberry Sauce:

- Cook a large batch of blueberry sauce and allow it to cool. Transfer the sauce to mason jars or other containers with tight-fitting lids. Store in the refrigerator for up to a week and use as a topping for pancakes, yogurt, or desserts.

Apple-Raspberry Crisp:

- Prepare the apple-raspberry crisp in a baking dish and bake according to the recipe. Once cooled, portion the crisp into individual servings and store them in airtight containers. Reheat in the oven or microwave before serving.

Nettle Pancakes with Raspberry Sauce:

- Make a batch of nettle pancakes and allow them to cool completely. Prepare raspberry sauce separately and store it in the refrigerator. When ready to eat, reheat the pancakes and serve with the raspberry sauce.

Apple Raspberry Crisp:

- Similar to the previous crisp, bake the apple raspberry crisp in a baking dish and allow it to cool. Portion into individual servings and store them in the refrigerator. Reheat in the oven or microwave before serving.

Raspberry Soy Muffins:

- Bake a batch of raspberry soy muffins and let them cool completely. Once cooled, store the muffins in an airtight container or freeze them for longer storage. Thaw frozen muffins overnight in the refrigerator or microwave them briefly before serving.

Chocolate Black Bean Brownies:

- Bake the chocolate black bean brownies and allow them to cool in the pan. Once cooled, cut them into squares and store them in an airtight container. They can be kept at room temperature for a few days or refrigerated for longer freshness.

SNACKS

Peanut Butter Banana Rice Cakes:

- Spread individual rice cakes with peanut butter and slice bananas. Store the rice cakes and banana slices separately in airtight containers in the refrigerator. Assemble the snack by topping each rice cake with banana slices just before eating.

Greek Yogurt Parfait:

- Prepare parfait components separately. Portion Greek yogurt into containers and store them in the refrigerator. Wash and chop fruits like berries or mangoes and store them in separate containers. Layer the yogurt and fruits in serving glasses or jars just before consuming.

Hummus Veggie Platter:

- Wash and cut assorted vegetables like carrots, cucumbers, bell peppers, and cherry tomatoes. Portion hummus into small containers or use a larger platter for sharing. Store the veggies and hummus separately in the refrigerator. Arrange the veggies around the hummus just before serving.

Tuna Cucumber Rounds:

- Prepare tuna salad by mixing canned tuna with mayonnaise or Greek yogurt, diced celery, and seasonings. Slice cucumbers into rounds. Store the tuna salad and cucumber rounds separately in the refrigerator. Spoon the tuna salad onto cucumber rounds just before eating.

Cinnamon Apple Slices:

- Prepare apple slices and toss them in lemon juice to prevent browning. Mix cinnamon and sugar in a small container. Sprinkle the cinnamon sugar mix over the apple slices just before eating.

Roasted Chickpeas:

- Drain and rinse canned chickpeas, then pat them dry. Toss chickpeas with olive oil and seasonings of your choice. Roast in the oven until crispy. Let them cool completely before storing in an airtight container.

Mixed Berry Cottage Cheese Bowl:

- Wash and portion mixed berries into containers. Portion cottage cheese into separate containers. Store both components in the refrigerator. Combine the berries and cottage cheese in a bowl just before eating.

Edamame Hummus:

- Prepare hummus using cooked and shelled edamame beans, garlic, lemon juice, tahini, and olive oil. Blend until smooth and store in an airtight container in the refrigerator. Serve with carrot sticks, cucumber slices, or whole grain crackers.

Avocado Toast:

- Slice and pit ripe avocados. Mash the avocado onto whole grain toast and sprinkle with salt and pepper. Pack the toast and avocado separately and assemble just before eating.

Mixed Nut and Seed Trail Mix:

- Mix together various nuts, seeds, and dried fruits in a large bowl. Portion the trail mix into individual snack bags or containers for easy grab-and-go snacks throughout the week.

BEVERAGE

Lime and Mint Infused Water:

- Fill a pitcher with water and add fresh lime slices and mint leaves. Let it infuse in the refrigerator for a few hours or overnight. Serve chilled over ice.

Berry Banana Chia Seed Smoothie:

- Prepare smoothie packs by portioning out mixed berries, banana slices, and chia seeds into individual freezer bags. Store them in the freezer. When ready to enjoy, simply blend the frozen ingredients with your choice of liquid (e.g., water, almond milk, or yogurt) until smooth.

Golden Turmeric Latte:

- Mix ground turmeric, cinnamon, ginger, and a pinch of black pepper in a small jar. Store this spice blend in a cool, dry place. When ready to make the latte, heat your choice of milk (e.g., almond milk or coconut milk) and whisk in the spice blend until well combined. Sweeten with honey or maple syrup if desired.

Carrot Ginger Juice:

- Juice fresh carrots and ginger root using a juicer. Store the juice in airtight containers in the refrigerator. Shake well before serving over ice.

Green Smoothie:

- Prepare smoothie packs by portioning out spinach, kale, banana slices, and any other desired fruits (e.g., pineapple or mango) into individual freezer bags. Store them in the freezer. When ready to enjoy, blend the frozen ingredients with your choice of liquid (e.g., coconut water or almond milk) until smooth.

Turmeric Golden Milk:

- Mix ground turmeric, cinnamon, ginger, and a pinch of black pepper in a small jar. Store this spice blend in a cool, dry place. When ready to make the golden milk, heat your choice of milk (e.g., almond milk or cow's milk) and whisk in the spice blend until well combined. Sweeten with honey or maple syrup if desired.

Mixed Berry Protein Smoothie:

- Prepare smoothie packs by portioning out mixed berries and protein powder into individual freezer bags. Store them in the freezer. When ready to enjoy, blend the frozen berries and protein powder with your choice of liquid (e.g., water or almond milk) until smooth.

Blueberry Compote:

- Cook fresh or frozen blueberries with a bit of water and honey or maple syrup in a saucepan until thickened. Let it cool before storing it in jars in the refrigerator. Serve over yogurt, oatmeal, or pancakes.

Green Tea Lemonade:

- Brew green tea and let it cool to room temperature. Mix the brewed tea with freshly squeezed lemon juice and sweeten with honey or agave syrup. Chill in the refrigerator before serving over ice.

Mango Green Tea Smoothie:

- Prepare smoothie packs by portioning out mango chunks and spinach leaves into individual freezer bags. Store them in the freezer. When ready to enjoy, blend the frozen mango and spinach with brewed green tea until smooth.

BONUS: RECIPE JOURNAL

RECIPE NAME:

PREP TIME:	COOK TIME:	SERVINGS

INGREDIENTS:

INSTRUCTIONS:

NOTES:

RECIPE NAME:

PREP TIME:	COOK TIME:	SERVINGS

INGREDIENTS:

INSTRUCTIONS:

NOTES:

RECIPE NAME:

PREP TIME: **COOK TIME:**   **SERVINGS**

INGREDIENTS:

INSTRUCTIONS:

NOTES:

RECIPE NAME:

PREP TIME: **COOK TIME:**   **SERVINGS**

INGREDIENTS:

INSTRUCTIONS:

NOTES:

RECIPE NAME:

PREP TIME: **COOK TIME:**   **SERVINGS**

INGREDIENTS:

INSTRUCTIONS:

NOTES:

RECIPE NAME:

PREP TIME: **COOK TIME:**   **SERVINGS**

INGREDIENTS:

INSTRUCTIONS:

NOTES:

RECIPE NAME:

PREP TIME: **COOK TIME:**   **SERVINGS**

INGREDIENTS:

INSTRUCTIONS:

NOTES:

RECIPE NAME:

PREP TIME: **COOK TIME:** **SERVINGS**

INGREDIENTS:

INSTRUCTIONS:

NOTES:

RECIPE NAME:

PREP TIME: **COOK TIME:**   **SERVINGS**

INGREDIENTS:

INSTRUCTIONS:

NOTES:

RECIPE NAME:

PREP TIME:	COOK TIME:	SERVINGS

INGREDIENTS:

INSTRUCTIONS:

NOTES:

Made in the USA
Columbia, SC
05 November 2024